POPULAR
ELECTRONIC
PROJECTS

ALSO BY THE SAME AUTHOR

POPULAR
ELECTRONIC
PROJECTS

by
R. A. PENFOLD

BERNARD BABANI (publishing) LTD
THE GRAMPIANS
SHEPHERDS BUSH ROAD
LONDON W6 7NF
ENGLAND

Although every care is taken with the preparation of this book, the publishers or author will not be responsible in any way for any errors that might occur.

Printed and Manufactured in Great Britain by
C. Nicholls & Co. Ltd.

CONTENTS

CHAPTER 1.

RADIO PROJECTS

This book has been written on the understanding that a collection of certain types of circuit will provide a number of designs to interest most electronics constructors, and although each reader will inevitably encounter some designs that are of little or no use to them, taken overall the book should be of considerable interest.

The selected projects cover a wide range of fields, such as audio, radio, metal detection, test equipment, and others. Since only a limited amount of space is available, some types of project have had to be left out. In general it is the more complicated designs which have been omitted, as it would take very few of these to fill a publication of this size. Also, with one or two exceptions, the cost and constructional difficulty of most of the more complicated projects is sufficiently discouraging to many constructors to take these projects out of the "highly popular" category.

MW Radio

A number of radio projects is the obvious starting point for a book such as this, simply because this is probably the most popular branch of amateur electronics. The field of radio is subdivided into many fields, some of which are very popular, and others that are of a specialised nature. Not surprisingly, ordinary AM MW/LW receivers seem to have the most universal appeal, with SW and radio control designs following them up. These are all covered here, starting with a simple medium wave radio.

The circuit diagram of the MW radio is shown in Fig. 1. This is a simple two transistor design which will provide good volume from many stations. It is primarily intended for use with a crystal earpiece, but it will also work well with high, medium, or low impedance moving coil headphones of reasonable sensitivity. It can also be used in conjunction with a separate amplifier and speaker to provide loudspeaker reception.

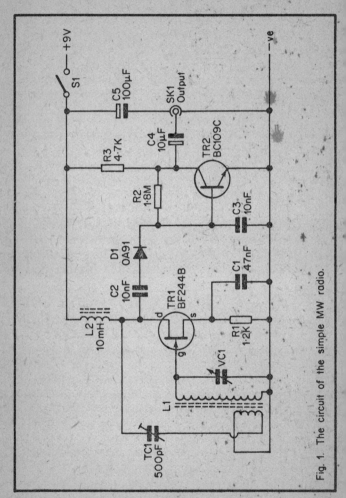

Fig. 1. The circuit of the simple MW radio.

A junction gate field effect transistor is used in the first stage of the unit, and this stage is an RF amplifier with preset regeneration. The main advantage of using a f.e.t. here, rather than an ordinary bipolar transistor, is that a f.e.t. has an extremely high input impedance and so the tuned circuit can be coupled direct to its input. In this case the tuned circuit consists of ferrite aerial L1 and tuning capacitor VC1. These are wired straight across the gate circuit of the f.e.t., Tr1, and the tuned winding of the ferrite aerial plays a secondary role by providing the gate bias for Tr1. R1 is the normal source bias resistor and C1 is its bypass capacitor. L2 is a ferrite corded choke which forms the drain load for Tr1.

The ferrite aerial is a ready made assembly which has a base coupling winding. As explained above, there is no need for such a coupling winding when using a f.e.t. This winding is not left unused however, but is used as a feedback winding. It is used to couple some of the output from Tr1 drain back to the ferrite aerial where it is passed back to the gate of Tr1 to be amplified for a second time. This is normally termed regeneration, or sometimes it is given the alternative name of reaction. TC1 provides DC blocking in the regeneration circuit, and it also permits the level of regeneration to be controlled.

If too much regeneration is applied to the circuit, Tr1 will begin to oscillate and proper reception will become impossible. Optimum results will be obtained with the regeneration level set to just below the threshold of oscillation. The feedback then boosts the gain of the RF stage by the maximum possible amount, and the selectivity of the set is similarly increased. The selectivity of a receiver is its ability to tune to just one of several closely spaced transmissions. In a simple TRF receiver such as this the level of selectivity is not very great without the use of regeneration, since only one tuned circuit is used. The boosted selectivity is therefore just as important as the increase in gain that the regeneration produces.

The output from the RF amplifier is coupled to diode detector D1 via DC blocking capacitor C2, and C3 is the RF smoothing capacitor. The audio signal developed across C3 is fed straight into the base circuit of Tr2, which is connected as a high gain, low noise, common emitter amplifier. R3 is its collector load resistor and R2 provides base biasing. C4 provides DC blocking at the output and C5 is a supply decoupling capacitor. S1 is an ordinary on/off switch.

Power can be obtained from any small 9 volt battery, such as a PP3 or a PP4, and the set is very economical to run as the current consumption is typically only about 2mA.

Notes

Constructionally the receiver should not prove to be very difficult, but there are one or two pit-falls which must be avoided. The set must be housed in a non-metallic case as otherwise the ferrite aerial will be screened by the case. The choke and the ferrite aerial should not be mounted too close to one another as they would then act as a form of transformer, which could either produce so much positive feedback that the circuit became unstable, or so much negative feedback that it became impossible to adjust TC1 for sufficient regeneration.

The specified ferrite aerial consists of a 127 x 9.5mm ferrite rod and a coil which fits this. If the set is to be miniaturised it will be necessary to replace the ferrite rod with a shorter one of the same diameter, or to shorten the rod that is supplied as part of the aerial. Using a rod of about 70mm or so in length will result in some loss of performance, but this will not be of any real significance. It is recommended that the ferrite rod should not be very much shorter than 70mm.

If the set is miniaturised it will obviously be necessary to have the choke and the ferrite aerial mounted fairly close together, which, as explained earlier, is likely to be detrimental. In order to minimise the feedback between these two components it is advisable to mount them at right angles to one another.

Do not mount the battery, (or any other mettalic object) very close to the aerial coil, as this will result in a screening affect on the aerial. The specified tuning capacitor is a fairly large type physically, and for a small or miniature set it would be preferable to use a small solid dielectric type having about the same value, or a slightly higher one. It is also possible to use a compression trimmer, the adjusting screw of this being replaced by a simple device known as a "trimmer converter".

If the set is to function properly it is essential that the connections to the ferrite aerial are correct. It is quite easy to find the two leads which form the main winding, and then determine which of these is the earthy lead and which is the "live" one. It is not so easy to determine the phasing of the smaller coil. Probably the easiest method is to use trial and error, with the coil initially being connected either way round. If regeneration cannot then be obtained, the connections to this winding should be reversed.

The receiver requires very little setting up and adjustment once it has been completed. TC1 should be adjusted to provide enough regeneration to enable a number of signals to be received, and then the coil is slid up and down the ferrite rod in order to obtain the correct frequency coverage. This is not too critical, and it is really just a matter of ensuring that there is no lack of coverage at either end of the MW band. The coil is then taped to the rod so that it cannot be accidentally moved.

TC1 is then adjusted for the highest value (screwed down as far as possible) that does not cause the RF amplifier to break into oscillation at any setting of VC1. It should be quite evident when oscillation occurs as a whistle of varying pitch will be heard from the earpiece as the set is tuned across a station. It is probably best not to be over critical when adjusting TC1, as the quality of the audio output will probably suffer if the regeneration is set right on the verge of oscillation. On the other hand, the level of regeneration must be quite close to the point at which oscillation occurs if really good results are to be obtained.

Medium Wave Radio Components

Resistors, all miniature ¼ watt 5 or 10%
R1   1.2k.
R2   1.8 Meg.
R3   4.7k.
Capacitors.
C1   47nf ceramic or plastic foil type.
C2   10nf plastic foil. VC1   Jackson Type 0 208 pf
C3   10nf plastic foil   air spaced (but see text).
C4   10mfd. 10v.w.   TC1   500pf compression trimmer
C5   100mfd. 10v.w.
Semiconductors.
Tr1   BF244B.
Tr2   BC109C.
D1   OA91.
Miscellaneous.
Denco MW/5FR ferrite aerial (L1).
Miniature SPST toggle or slider switch (S1).
10mH. ferrite cored choke, Repanco type or similar (L2).
PP3 battery, control knob, case, etc.

MW Superhet

Superhet receivers are considerably more complicated than
TRF ones, both to construct and to adjust when completed.
Superhet designs offer a high degree of performance though,
and it is likely that a simple superhet is capable of out-perform-
ing the best of the TRF designs. All commercially produced
transistor radios now seem to be of the superhet variety. The
circuit diagram of a MW superhet receiver is shown in Fig.2,
and although this design only uses three active devices, the use
of two high performance ICs ensures that excellent results are
obtained.

Tr1 is used as the basis of a conventional mixer oscillator stage.
L1 is the ferrite aerial, the tuned winding of which is tuned
over the MW band by means of VC1. Received RF signals are

coupled to the base of Tr1 by way of a low impedance coupling winding and DC blocking capacitor C1. T1 is the oscillator transformer, and this causes Tr1 to oscillate by supplying positive feedback between its collector and emitter terminals (Tr1 operates in the grounded base mode as far as the oscillator circuitry is concerned). The third (tuned) winding of T1 determines the oscillator frequency in conjunction with the oscillator tuning capacitor, VC2. This is ganged with VC1. C4 is the usual padder capacitor, and TC1 and TC2 are alignment trimmers. The latter are part of the specified tuning capacitor.

The purpose of the mixer/oscillator stage is to convert the incoming signal to the intermediate frequency of the set. In this case the IF is about 465 to 470kHz, and IFT1 is tuned to receive the IF signal. In a TRF receiver it is the aerial tuned circuit which provides the selectivity of the set, but in a superhet receiver it is the IF tuned circuits that determine the bandwidth. Here a double tuned IF transformer contains the only IF tuned circuits, but this still provides a far higher level of selectivity than does the ferrite aerial. If a higher level of selectivity is required, it is merely necessary to use a Toko CFT470C ceramic filter in place of the Denco IF transformer.

A ZN414 IC is used as the basis of the IF amplifier, and it also provides the detector and automatic gain control (AGC) circuitry. This device is very well known to most amateur electronics enthusiasts, but it is usually used as the basis of a TRF receiver. However, it works very well as an IF amplifier, and a set such as this can easily outperform a ZN414 based TRF set. The reason for this is the increased gain that is provided by the mixer/oscillator stage, and the increased selectivity that is introduced by the IF filtering.

Diodes D1 and D2 are used as low voltage Zener diodes, and they provide a stabilised voltage of approximately 1.3 volts which is used to power the ZN414 circuitry. The audio output from the ZN414 is fed to the volume control (VR1) via a simple RF filter which uses C6, R8, and C7, and by way of DC blocking capacitor C8. Good RF filtering is needed in order to avoid instability in the audio stages of the receiver.

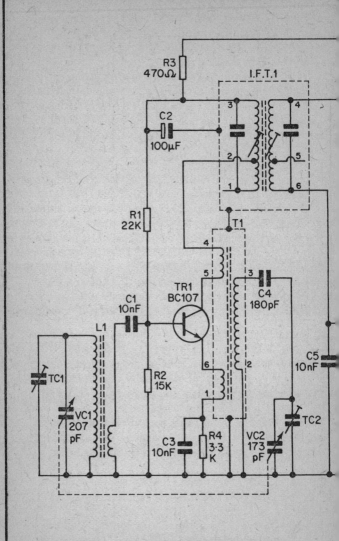

Fig. 2. The circuit diagram of the MW Superhet receiver.

14

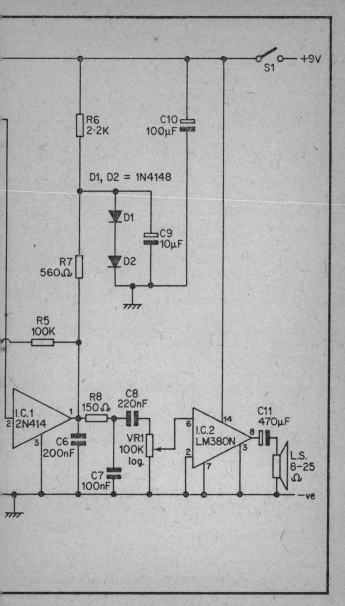

The audio stages of the set employ an LM380N audio power amplifier IC. An attractive feature of the device is that is needs very few discrete components to produce a practical audio amplifier. For instance, no DC blocking capacitor is needed between the input and the volume control. The LM380N actually has two inputs, an inverting one (pin 6) and a non-inverting one (pin 2). In this case it is the inverting input which is used, and the non-inverting input is connected to earth in order to avoid the possibility of instability due to stray feedback from the output.

DC blocking is provided at the output by C11. The LM380N has its voltage gain set at typically 50 times by its internal feedback circuitry, and this level of gain is just about right for this application. Speakers having an impedance in the range 8 to 15 ohms can be used with the circuit, and the maximum available output power depends upon the speaker impedance used. An 8 ohm speaker provides the greatest output, the actual figure being approximately 300mW. This falls to about 100mW if a 25 ohm speaker is used.

S1 is the on/off switch, and this can be ganged with VR1 if required. C2, C9 and C10, and R3 are the supply decoupling components. The quiescent current consumption of the set is about 8mA or so, and this increases to about 40 to 50 mA at high volume levels (the LM380N has a class B output stage).

Alignment

Constructionally the set should provide few problems, but remember to use a non-metallic case and to keep large metallic components (such as the tuning capacitor and the battery), a reasonable distance away from the ferrite aerial. Connection details for the coils are not provided here as they are usually supplied with the coils.

Initially the trimmers on the tuning capacitor should be well screwed down, and the cores of T1 and IFT1 should be left alone. By adjusting the tuning control it should be possible to tune to a few stations, and these can be peaked by adjusting the position of the coil on the ferrite rod. It is difficult to aurally adjust the set to peak signals due to the AGC action of the ZN414, but a visual indication of the strength of received signals can be obtained by connecting a multimeter set to a low volts range across C7. Suitable voltage ranges would be something like 2.5 or 5 volts f.s.d., and the negative test prod connects to earth (the negative supply rail). Maximum signal strength corresponds to the minimum meter reading.

When a station has been located and the aerial coil has been peaked, the cores of the IF transformer or filter are peaked. The Toko ceramic filter can have its cores adjusted using a screwdriver provided care is exercised, but the Denco IFT should only be adjusted using a proper trimming tool, such as the Denco TT5. A screwdriver could easily damage the cores. If no multimeter is available, adjustments can be made on a weak station, with the cores being adjusted for maximum volume. Make sure that the set is accurately tuned to the station before the IF adjustments are made. Note that the filter should require very little adjustment as they are supplied prealigned.

Next TC2 is adjusted to provide the set with the correct frequency coverage. This is really just a matter of adjusting it to a setting where no stations are lost due to a lack of coverage at the high frequency end of the band (the vanes of the tuning capacitor almost fully unmeshed), and that the coverage does not extend into the marine band. It is probably best to make this adjustment at night, as after dark a great many stations will be received, and the high frequency band limit is usually very easily located. It is important that this adjustment is made fairly accurately as otherwise it might not be possible to align the aerial circuit satisfactorily.

This aerial alignment is carried out in the following manner. First tune to a station at the low frequency end of the band and adjust the position of the coil on the ferrite rod to peak this signal. Then tune to a station at the high frequency end of the band and adjust TC1 to peak the signal. Then retune

17

to the station at the low frequency end of the band and read-just the aerial coil to peak the signal again. Retune to the station at the high frequency end of the band, and repeat this whole procedure a few times until no further adjustment is necessary.

It is unlikely that alignment will be perfect over the entire band, but the sensitivity of the set should be good over the complete MW band. If the position of the coil on the ferrite aerial seems to be excessively critical then this probably means that the coupling winding on the coil is connected with the wrong phasing. Its connections should be reversed in order to correct this.

Medium Wave Superhet Receiver Components

Resistors, all miniature ¼ watt 5 or 10%.

R1	22k.	R5	100k.
R2	15k.	R6	2.2k.
R3	470 ohms.	R7	560 ohms.
R4	3.3k.	R8	150 ohms.
VR1	10k. log. carbon.		

Capacitors.

C1	10nf plastic foil.
C2	100mfd. 10v.w.
C3	10nf plastic foil.
C4	180pf ceramic plate.
C5	10nf plastic foil.
C6	220nf ceramic or plastic foil.
C7	100nf ceramic or plastic foil.
C8	220nf ceramic or plastic foil.
C9	10mfd. 10v.w.
C10	100mfd. 10v.w.
C11	470mfd. 10v.w.
VC1/2	Jackson 208pf plus 176pf air spaced variable type 00, with built in trimmers (TC1 and TC2).

Semiconductors.
Tr1   BC107
IC1   ZN414.
IC2   LM380N.
D1 &
D2   IN4148 (2 off), or any similar silicon diodes.

Inductors.
L1   Denco MW/5FR ferrite aerial.
T1   Denco TOC.1 oscillator coil.
IFT1   Denco IFT18/465kHz or Toko CFT470C.

Miscellaneous.
8 to 25 ohm impedance loudspeaker.
SPST slider switch or miniature toggle switch (S1), or can be
ganged with VR1.
9 volt battery control knobs, etc.
Addition components for MW/LW version.
Denco MW/LW/5FR ferrite aerial (replaces MW/5FR type).
SPDT miniature toggle switch (S2).
250pf compression trimmer (TC3).

MW/LW Version

It is an easy matter to convert the receiver to MW and LW
operation, and is it merely necessary to replace the Denco
MW/5FR ferrite aerial with a MW/LW/5FR type, and add a
few extra components. The necessary modification is shown in
the circuit diagram of Fig.3.

There is an additional coil on the ferrite aerial, and in the MW
position S2 short circuits this winding so that it has no significant effect on the circuit. When S2 is in the LW position this
short is removed and the increased inductance in the aerial coil
circuitry provides coverage of the LW band. TC3 is shunted
across the oscillator tuning capacitance, and this provides the
necessary reduction in the operating frequency of this part of
the circuit.

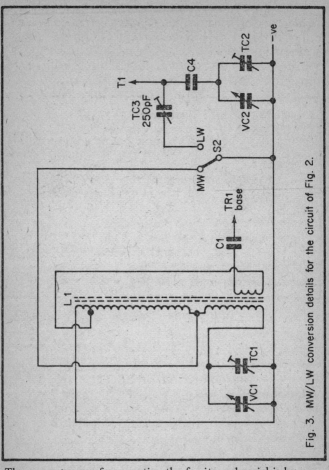

Fig. 3. MW/LW conversion details for the circuit of Fig. 2.

The correct way of connecting the ferrite rod aerial is by no means immediately obvious, and the connection diagram given in Fig. 4 should be of help to constructors.

Initially the MW/LW version of the receiver is aligned in precisely the same way as the basic version is. When the MW alignment has been completed the receiver is switched to the LW band and the tuning is set at the central position. TC3 is then adjusted to tune in Radio 2 on 1500 Metres, and it might be necessary to experiment a little with the position of the LW coil on the ferrite rod before it is possible to receive this station. When it has been accurately tuned in, slide the LW coil up and down the rod to find the position that gives the strongest signal.

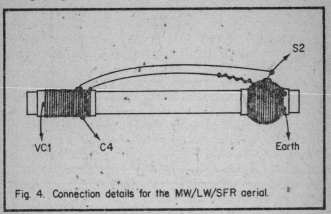

Fig. 4. Connection details for the MW/LW/SFR aerial.

The alignment is then complete, but it is advisable to repeat both the MW and LW aerial alignment at least once as the position of the LW coil on the ferrite rod does have some effect on MW alignment and vice versa. Once the set is performing well on both bands the coils can be carefully taped to the rod, or alternatively some adhesive (such a Denco Denfix) can be used.

SW Converter

There can be little doubt that for serious SW reception a sophisticated communications receiver is almost a necessity with the overcrowding that occurs on the SW bands. However, such sets are very expensive to buy ready-made, and it is a major task to construct one's own (such a design certainly goes beyond the scope of this book). On the other hand, a lot of fun and useful experience can be obtained from building and using relatively simple and inexpensive SW equipment, and many distant (DX) stations can be received using such equipment, despite the comparative limitations of such a receiving set-up.

Probably the most common type of simple SW receiver is the regenerative TRF type, and these are excellent for general SW listening. There are alternative approaches, a common one being to use, a SW converter in conjunction with an ordinary MW broadcast receiver. Both of these are covered here, starting with a SW converter. It should perhaps be pointed out that this type of receiving set-up is not really suitable for amateur bands listening as an ordinary AM receiver is unsuitable for single sideband (SSB) and CW (Morse) reception, and these are the two main transmitting modes which are used on the SW amateur bands. The TRF receiver which is described later in this book is more suitable for such reception. A SW converter and MW receiver combination will usually provide very good results on the SW broadcast bands.

The circuit diagram of the SW converter is shown in Fig. 5. The purpose of the converter is to convert received signals to a frequency of 1.6MHz, and then locally radiate them at this frequency. A MW receiver tuned to 1.6MHz and placed close to the radiator coil will obviously pick-up the radiated SW signals, and then process them to produce an audio output. The level of performance obtained depends upon several factors, the main ones being the level of sensitivity and selectivity that the receiver has, and how well the output of the converter is coupled to the receiver. As most MW receivers are now reasonably sophisticated, good results will almost certainly be obtained provided converter to receiver coupling is obtained.

The circuit of the converter is divided into two main sections: the mixer stage which is built around Tr1, and the oscillator stage which is based on Tr2. The oscillator circuit is arranged to operate at a frequency that is always 1.6MHz higher than the frequency of the received signal. The received signal and the

22

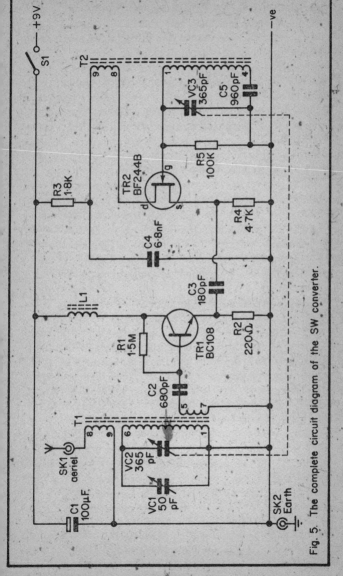

Fig. 5. The complete circuit diagram of the SW converter.

23

oscillator signal are then heterodyned in the mixer to produce the sum and difference frequencies. It is the difference signal that is required here, as this must be at 1.6MHz since the oscillator is always 1.6MHz higher in frequency than the received signal. The MW receiver picks up this signal and processes it, but it ignores any other output signals that are produced since these lay outside its passband. The converter really just provides the same action as the mixer/oscillator stages of an ordinary superhet receiver, and the converter and receiver combination forms a type of double superhet receiver arrangement.

TR1 is basically just a common emitter amplifier having an unbypassed emitter resistor (R2). T1 is the input transformer which has an aerial coupling winding and a base coupling winding, the latter connects to TR1 base via DC blocking capacitor C2. The tuned winding of T1 is tuned over a frequency range of about 5 to 15MHz (60 to 20 metres) by VC2. VC1 is an aerial trimmer control, and this eliminates the need for any complicated alignment of the finished converter.

The oscillator uses a simple inductive feedback circuit. The specified oscillator coil was originally intended for use in valved circuits, but f.e.t.s have certain important similarities to valves, and so this circuit works perfectly well. VC3 is the oscillator tuning capacitor, and this is ganged with VC2. C5 is the oscillator padder capacitor, and the coil manufacturer specifies a value of 960pf for use in this position. Such a value does not seem to be readily available to the amateur, and it would take several preffered value capacitors wired in parallel to make up this value. Since the converter is fitted with an aerial trimmer control, tracking between the aerial and oscillator tuned circuits would not seem to be very critical, and satisfactory results can be obtained by using two 470pf capacitors connected in parallel in the C5 position. Even using a 1,000pf (1nf) component seemed to give satisfactory results.

The oscillator output is developed across the unbypassed source resistor, R4, and this signal is coupled to the emitter of Tr1 by

C3. Here it has the effect of modulating the emitter — base voltage of Tr1, and this results in variations in its collector current. The gain of Tr1 varies to some extent with changes in collector current, and so the oscillator signal modulates the aerial signal to produce the required mixing and heterodyne effect. The 1.6MHz output signal is developed across L1, which is the radiator coil.

C1, C4 and R3 are supply decoupling components and S1 is the ordinary on/off switch. The unit can be powered from a small 9 volt battery such as a PP3 as the current consumption of the unit is only about 2mA.

Construction and Use

The form of construction favoured by the author for this type of project is point to point wiring. The two coils have polystyrene formers, and it is not a good idea to make connections direct to the pins which are moulded into the base of the former, as the polystyrene tends to melt. The coils will plug into B9A valveholders, and it is recommended that these are mounted on the chassis of the unit and that the connections are made to the pins of the holders. Otherwise, unused pins can be used to provide anchor points for the transistors, capacitors, etc., and additional anchor points, if required, can be provided by tagstrips. The wiring should all be kept reasonably short and direct.

The radiator coil, L1, is home-made and consists of about 30 turns of 24 SWG enamelled copper wire wound in a single layer around the middle section of a 1 inch x ¼ inch ferrite rod. Note however, that this is not a tuned winding and is not at all critical. About 30 turns of any insulated wire wound around the middle of any ferrite rod would probably provide adequate results.

Although not essential, it is advisable to fit a slow motion drive to the tuning capacitor, as otherwise tuning will be rather difficult. This is due to the wide range of frequencies that are covered. Of primary interest to the short wave listener will be the four broadcast bands that are included in the coverage of the converter. These are the 25, 31, 41, and 49 Metre bands. It may also be possible to locate the 19 Metre band at the extreme high frequency end of the units coverage, and the 60 Metre band at the extreme LF end.

The converter is intended to be used with a proper outdoor aerial, and this can consist of about 10 to 40 Metres of aerial wire strung between any two convenient points. It is preferable for the aerial to be set as high up as possible and kept well clear of buildings and other large obstructions (although it is only very rarely that this ideal can be achieved). An indoor aerial about 10 Metres long can also be used, but results will obviously not be as good as when using a proper outdoor type. If an earth connection is available this can be connected to SK1, but at the frequencies involved here an earth is likely to be of very little benefit, and is not important.

As supplied, the two coils have their cores screwed right in for packing purposes, and the cores should be unscrewed so that about 10mm of screw thread protrudes from the top of each coil. The radiator coil must be placed close to the ferrite aerial of the MW receiver, and the two ferrite rods should be parallel to one another. Usually the ferrite aerial is near the case of the set, and so a good signal transfer can be obtained with the radiator coil mounted on the outside of the radio, opposite the aerial. Bostik Blue Tak or double sided adhesive tape can be used to hold the radiator coil in position. The MW receiver is tuned to a frequency of about 1.6MHz (just about the extreme high frequency end of the band), and it does not have to be tuned very precisely to this frequency. The converter can be adjusted to compensate for any error in this respect.

With the receiver and the converter both switched on, it should be possible to tune a few stations by adjusting the tuning control of the converter. The receiver must obviously be tuned to a quiet spot on the MW band as otherwise stations received directly by the receiver will interfere with the output from the converter. It may be difficult to find a quiet spot on the band after darkness has fallen, but it should be possible, and remember that a ferrite rod is directional, and the set can be rotated to null any interfering signal. Once a clear signal is obtained from the converter, the core of L1 can be adjusted so that the VC1 can peak received signals at any setting of the tuning control. This is largely a matter of trial and error, but the core will probably need to be unscrewed somewhat from its present position. The position of the radiator coil can then be adjusted to find the one that provides the greatest signal transfer.

It is not hard to locate the broadcast bands when using the unit: in fact it is difficult to overlook them when propagation conditions are good. On the bands covered by the converter, results will normally be best after dark, although on the 19 Metre band (and perhaps the 25 Metre band occasionally) results will be best during daylight hours. Reception of stations many thousands of miles away should be possible when conditions are good.

Short Wave Converter Components

Resistors, all miniature ¼ watt 5 or 10%.
R1   1.5 Meg.
R2   220 ohms.
R3   1.8k.
R4   4.7k.
R5   100k.

Capacitors
C1   100mfd. 10v.w.
C2   680pf ceramic plate.
C3   180pf ceramic plate.
C4   6.8nf ceramic or plastic foil.
C5   960pf (see text) ceramic plate, or mica, or
        polystyrene.
VC1   50pf airspaced variable (Jackson type C804).
VC2/3   365pf plus 365pf airspaced (Jackson type O).

Inductors.

T1   Denco transistor coil Range 4T blue.
T2   Denco Dual Purpose coil Range 4 White.
L1   Home-made, see text for details.

Semiconductors.
Tr1   BC108.
Tr2   BF244B.

Miscellaneous.
SPST toggle switch (S1).
Two B9A valveholders (used as coilholders).
Aerial and earth sockets.
Case, control knob, 9 volt battery, etc.

SW Receiver

Fig. 6 shows the complete circuit diagram of the TRF SW
receiver. This is suitable for either fixed operation using a
longwire antenna, or portable use if a telescopic aerial is
employed. The receiver has a frequency coverage of approximately 1.6 to 15MHz in two ranges. The output is primarily
intended for use with high impedance (2,000 or 4,000 ohms)
magnetic headphones, but it will also work quite well in conjunction with a crystal earpiece or lower impedance magnetic
headphones.

TR1 is used as a regenerative detector, and this type of detector
relies upon the fact that a transistor (of the type used here
anyway) has a gain that increases with increasing collector
current. Thus Tr1 will provide more gain on negative going
output half cycles (which cause an increase in collector
current) than it will on positive going ones (which cause a
reduction in collector current). A form of rectification and
detection is therefore provided by the circuit.

Tr1 is biased by R1, and at RF its collector load is formed by
L1. T1 is the input transformer, and the received signals are

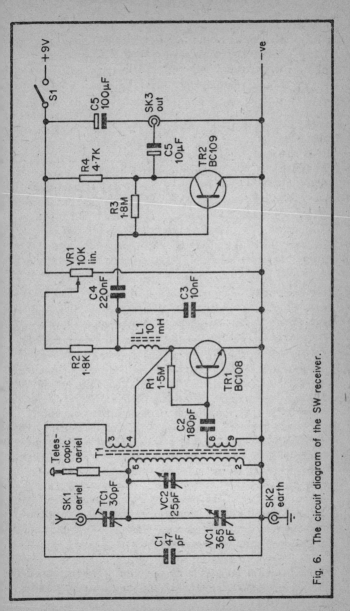

Fig. 6. The circuit diagram of the SW receiver.

29

coupled into the base of Tr1 by way of the low impedance base winding and DC. blocking capacitor C2. VC1 is the tuning capacitor, or bandset capacitor as it is sometimes termed in this context, and VC2 is the bandspread control. This term will be more fully explained later on.

The telescopic aerial, if used, couples direct to the non-earthy end of the tuned circuit. This very tight coupling is necessary as there is not a great deal of signal pick-up in a telescopic aerial. If a longwire antenna is used, it is coupled to the tuned circuit via TC1. This trimmer limits the degree of coupling between the aerial and the tuned circuit, and without this component the aerial would excessively load the tuned circuit. This would result in a loss of selectivity, and could also prevent the detector from operating correctly. It should perhaps be pointed out that it is possible to incorporate both a telescopic aerial and an external aerial socket in the receiver, but the telescopic aerial should be retracted when the longwire aerial is in use.

Regeneration is provided between the collector of Tr1 and T1 via the third winding on T1. C1 is needed for DC blocking, As explained in an earlier section, regeneration increases both the gain and the selectivity of a receiver. When a regenerative detector is used (rather than just a regenerative RF amplifier followed by a conventional diode detector) it also has the effect of increasing the detection efficiency. The reason for this is that there is more feedback on negative going output half cycles, because Tr1 has a higher gain on these half cycles in comparison with the positive going half cycles. The regeneration thus increases the inequality in the degree of amplification afforded to each set of half cycles, and so also increases the detection efficiency.

The audio output of the detector is developed across R2, and C3 provides the necessary RF filtering. VR1 is the regeneration control, and this enables the regeneration level to be adjusted by varying the supply voltage to Tr1 and its associated circuitry. C4 couples the audio output of the detector to the base of Tr2, which is connected as a high gain, low noise, common emitter amplifier. It is biased by R3 and R4 is its collector load resistor. C5 provides DC blocking at the output and C6 is a supply decoupling capacitor. S1 is the on/off switch, and this can be ganged with VR1 if desired. Power can be obtained from a small 9 volt battery such as a PP3 or PP4 as the current consumption of the receiver is typically less than 2mA.

Construction And Use

Most simple SW receivers that are designed to cover more than one range use plug-in bandchanging. This is where the desired range is selected by merely plugging the appropriate coil into the coilholder. In this case the coilholder is a B9A valveholder. If frequent bandchanging is likely to be necessary it will obviously be necessary to choose a form of construction that will permit easy access to the coilholder.

Alternatively, as in this particular case, there are only two coils having three windings each, bandswitching is not really much of a problem. It can be accomplished using the simple modification shown in the circuit diagram of Fig. 7. If bandswitching is used, it is essential to keep the wiring associated with the bandswitch fairly short, as otherwise stray capacitance could possibly upset the operation of the circuit.

Whatever form of bandswitching is used; it is probably best to use point to point wiring in the construction of the RF circuitry, and Veroboard or other popular forms of construction are perfectly suitable for the AF circuitry.

As supplied, the cores of the coils are screwed right in, and they must be unscrewed so that about 10mm of metal screw thread is visible at the top of each coil. If the telescopic aerial is the only type of aerial that is to be used, no further adjustment is needed before the receiver is ready for use. If a long-wire aerial is to be used, TC1 should initially be adjusted for minimum capacitance. When some experience has been gained with the set it can be experimentally tried at higher settings, but be careful not to use too high a capacitance here. This will result in a noticeable loss of selectivity, with weak stations being drowned by strong ones, even if the stations are well separated.

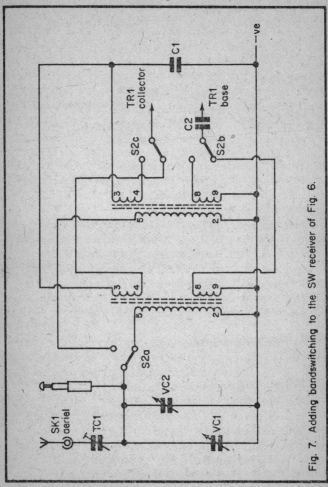

Fig. 7. Adding bandswitching to the SW receiver of Fig. 6.

When first trying out the receiver it is probably best to use the Range 4 coil as there will usually be a number of strong signals within this range of frequencies. With VR1 slightly advanced it should be possible to tune in a few stations using VC1, and further advancing VR1 should increase the volume from these stations. However, if VR1 is advanced too far, the detector will break into oscillation and proper reception of AM signals will not be possible. A whistle will be heard on AM signals. CW and SSB signals (which are used extensively on the SW amateur bands) can be resolved with the detector adjusted beyond the threshold of oscillation. In fact, this is the only way such transmissions can be resolved by a receiver such as this.

It will probably be found to be rather difficult to tune accurately to stations using the bandset control (VC1) as it covers a very wide range of frequencies. The set will thus be tuned over numerous stations by adjusting the control knob of VC1 through only a few degrees. Bandspread capacitor VC2 is incorporated in the design in order to overcome this problem.

In use, the bandset control is adjusted to the part of the tuning range which is to be scanned for stations, but then the actual tuning is carried out using the bandspread control. As VC2 has a much lower value than VC1, the bandspread control will only cover a small part of the band, and so tuning using this control will be far less cramped than when using the bandset one.

The Range 3 coil covers a frequency range of approximately 1.6 to 5.5MHz, and this is generally known as the Trawler Band. Apart from maritime transmissions, the 80 and 160 Metre amateur bands can also be received on this range. The frequency coverage using the Range 4 coil is from about 5 to 15MHz. Of primary interest here are the 40 and 20 Metre amateur bands, the latter offering the best opportunities for DX (distant) reception. Also there are the 25, 31, 41 and 49 Metre Broadcast Bands.

SW Receiver Components

Resistors, all are miniature ¼ watt 5 or 10%.

R1   1.5 Meg.
R2   1.8k.
R3   1.8 Meg.
R4   4.7k.
VR1   10k lin. carbon.

Capacitors.

C1   47pf ceramic plate or polystyrene.
C2   180pf ceramic plate.
C3   10nf plastic foil.
C4   220nf plastic foil.
C5   10mfd. 10v.w.
C6   100mfd. 10v.w.
VC1   365pf air spaced (Jackson Type 0).
VC2   25pf air spaced (Jackson type C804).
TC1   3/30pf miniature trimmer, or any similar type.

Inductors

T1   Denco D.P. Green coils Ranges 3 and (or) 4 (see text).
L1   10mH. choke (Repanco type CH4).

Semiconductors

Tr1   BC108.
Tr2   BC109.

Miscellaneous.

SPST toggle switch (S1).
B9A valveholder(s).
Aerial and earth sockets.
Telescopic aerial, if required.
4 way 3 pole rotary switch (S2) with adjustable end stop (set for two way operation, only needed if bandswitching is employed).
Case, control knobs, 9 volt battery, etc.

Field Strength Monitor For 27MHz

Three pieces of radio control equipment will be described here; a transmitter, a receiver, and a field strength monitor.

A field strength monitor is simply a device which gives an indication of the strength of the RF field generated by the transmitter. Its purpose is to enable a transmitter to be tuned up for maximum output. Such units are often passive devices which rely on a strong signal being received, and without such a signal they give little or no meter deflection. Such monitors have the advantage of being simple and requiring no power source such as a battery, but they can sometimes be difficult to use since radio control transmitters are often extremely low powered. For this reason a simple but sensitive active circuit is described here. The circuit diagram of the unit appears in Fig. 8.

The signal received by the telescopic aerial is directly coupled to the tuned circuit which is comprised of VC1 and the main winding of T1. The 27MHz band (which extends from 29.96 to 27.28MHz) is covered with VC1 at around half maximum capacitance. The unit actually covers considerably more than 27MHz band, and it has been purposely designed this way so that any misadjustment of the unit will not prevent it from covering the appropriate frequency range.

Tr1 is used as a common emitter RF amplifier, and it has L1 as its collector load with R1 providing the base bias. The tuned circuit is coupled to the base of Tr1 via a low impedance winding on T1 and DC blocking capacitor C1. There is a third winding on T1, but this is not used here and is simply ignored.

The output from the RF amplifier is coupled to a diode pump circuit which utilises C2, D1, and D2. The pulsed DC output of this circuit is fed to a meter via a variable attenuator of the volume control type (VR1). The latter is virtually essential on a sensitive monitor such as this as it can easily be overloaded by a reasonably strong transmitter. A smoothing capacitor of about 10nf could be used across the output of the diode pump circuit in the conventional manner, but this does not seem to have any effect on performance.

S1 is the on/off switch, and power is obtained from a small 9 volt dry battery such as a PP3. The current consumption of the unit is about 8mA.

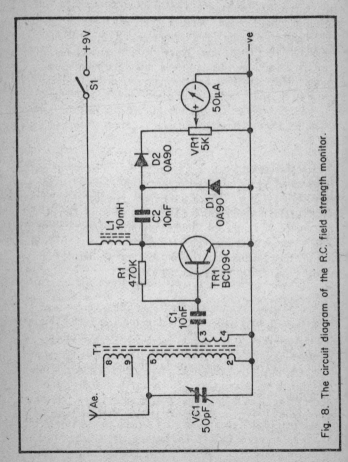

Fig. 8. The circuit diagram of the R.C. field strength monitor.

Construction And Use.

Like the Denco coils employed in some of the previous designs, T1 has a base which fits into a B9A valveholder, and it is advisable to mount it in one of these rather than solder direct to the pins of the coil. It is possible to make connections direct to the pins, but it is necessary to complete the joints quickly as the polystyrene coil will otherwise tend to melt with the heat from the soldering iron. The core of the coil should be unscrewed so that roughly 10mm of metal screw thread protrudes from the top of the coil.

Point to point wiring is probably the best form of construction for this very simple project, but it is necessary to keep the wiring reasonably short and direct whatever constructional form is used.

Ideally the meter should be a reasonably large 50 micro-amp. unit, but these are rather expensive. It is quite acceptable to use a cheaper, smaller alternative such as a tuning or battery level meter, as in this case the scaling of the meter is unimportant. It is merely required to give an indication of whether an adjustment to a transmitter causes an increase or decrease in field strength. Most of these meters have a sensitivity of less than 50 micro-amps, with sensitivities usually being in the range 100 to 500 micro-amps. This does not matter too much, and using a less sensitive meter will just result in the monitor being a little sensitive.

A monitor such as this is most commonly used when tuning up a transmitter for maximum output. It can also be used to show whether or not some modification to a transmitter has increased the output power. However, when doing this it is essential to make sure that the two sets of tests are done under identical conditions (same distance between transmitter and monitor, same orientation of aerials, VR1 in the same position, etc.).

R.C. Field Strength Monitor Components

R1   470k ¼ watt 5 or 10%.
VR1   5k lin. carbon.
C1   10nf plastic foil.
C2   10nf plastic foil.
VC1   50pf air spaced (Jackson type C804).
Tr1   BC109C.
D1   OA90.
D2   OA90.
T1   Denco Green DP coil Range 5.
L1   10mH. choke (Repanco CH4).
M1   50 micro-amp. moving coil meter, size and type is
            unimportant (see text).
S1   SPST toggle type. Telescopic Aerial.
Case, battery, etc.

Radio Control Receiver

It is normal for at least one piece of equipment in a radio
control link to be crystal controlled, as this virtually guarantees
that the equipment is operating within the legal band limits.
In fact it is normal for both the transmitter and the receiver
to be crystal controlled. Although this may seem to be rather
expensive and extravagant on the face of it, it is really quite
practical. For one thing, sets of radio control crystals can be
obtained quite cheaply; probably for no more than the cost
of a single crystal. A second advantage of dual crystal control
is that it ensures that the transmitter and receiver stay tuned
to a common frequency, as crystals cannot be detuned by
vibration in the same way as a variable inductor or trimmer
capacitor can. Only very slight detuning of the receiver's or
transmitter's oscillator would be needed in order to render the
system ineffective.

The system described here is a simple single channel type where at switch on the transmitter causes a relay to close at the receiver. Apart from some obvious and simple control applications, it is possible to obtain quite sophisticated control of a model by using the receiver in conjunction with a suitable actuator. It would probably be possible for experienced constructors to modify the unit to operate as the RC link for a more sophisticated system, but the author has not tried this. The link has only been tested up to ranges of about 100 metres, and due to the low transmitter power used this almost certainly represents about the maximum reliable range that can be attained. However, the system is only really intended for the control of a land model or a model boat, and so a range of 100 metres is more than adequate. Both the transmitter and receiver are crystal controlled.

Fig. 9 shows the complete circuit diagram of the radio control receiver. This is a simple superhet circuit, and Tr1 is used as the basis of the mixer stage. This is a Jugfet which is used in the common source amplifying mode. The aerial is directly coupled to the tuned circuit which uses L1 and C2. In turn, the tuned circuit is direct coupled into the gate circuit of Tr1.

Tr2 is used in the local oscillator stage, and this uses the common collector Colpitts crystal oscillator configuration. The output from the oscillator is fed to the gate circuit of Tr1 via C14. As Tr1 does not act as a perfectly linear amplifier, the oscillator signal causes variations in the gain of Tr1, and provides the required mixing action.

The IF output is developed across the untuned winding of IFT1. Of course, this winding would normally be used as the secondary one, but in this application it must be used in reverse if good results are to be obtained.

In order to produce the required 470kHz IF output, crystal X1 must have a frequency which is 470kHz lower than the crystal used in the transmitter. These crystals are readily available as matched pairs, and this is the best way to obtain them. Crystal pairs intended for an IF of 455 or 465kHz are

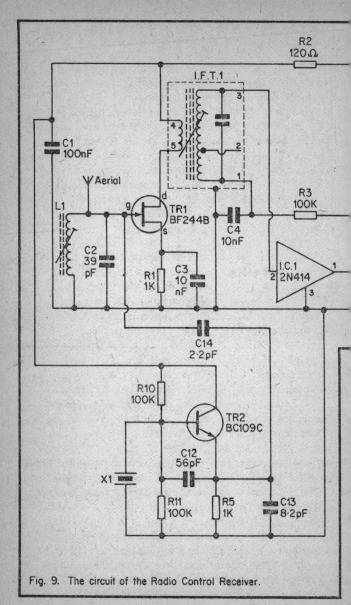

Fig. 9. The circuit of the Radio Control Receiver.

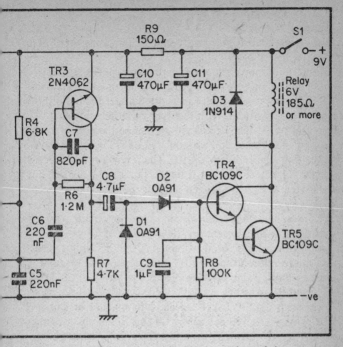

also suitable, as IFT1 will readily tune to either of these frequencies. It does not matter what the transmitter frequency is, provided it is within the legal band limits, and the appropriate receiver crystal frequency is used. The input tuned circuit can be peaked to any frequency within the 27MHz RC band.

It should perhaps be explained that RC crystals are usually third overtone types. This means that their nominal operating frequency is one third of the marked frequency, but the crystal is designed to operate at the marked frequency if a tuned circuit resonant at this frequency is included in the oscillator circuit to suppress oscillation at the fundamental frequency. For the sake of simplicity, in this circuit no such tuned circuit is included, and so the oscillator operates at about 9MHz. This is quite satisfactory in practice as the oscillator produces plenty of harmonic output, and the third harmonic provides the required signal at about 27MHz.

The IF amplifier uses a ZN414 IC which is ideal for this purpose as it enables a good high gain IF amplifier, detector, and AGC circuit to be easily condensed into a small space.

The form of modulation used in this system is keyed amplitude modulation, or type A2 emission as it is sometimes known. This form of modulation is permitted under the radio control licencing conditions. With this type of modulation the transmitter normally transmits an unmodulated carrier wave, but an audio tone can be modulated onto the carrier wave by operating a push button switch. The receiver must be designed so that a relay connected at the output is normally off, but is activated when a modulated signal is received.

Tr3 is used as a high gain, common emitter amplifier of conventional design, except for the inclusion of C7 which is used to provide a degree of high frequency roll-off, and is needed in order to prevent instability. The output of Tr3 is used to drive a diode pump circuit which is comprised of C8, D1, D2 C9, and R8. When an unmodulated signal is received, no significant signal is fed to the diode pump, and virtually no DC voltage is developed across C9 and R8. Modulating the signal causes quite a high amplitude audio signal to be fed into the pump circuit, and the voltage produced across C9 and R8 by this signal will be sufficient to turn on the common emitter Darlington Pair formed by Tr4 and Tr5. These have the relay as their collector load, and so they will supply power to the relay coil. When the modulation is switched off, C9 will quickly discharge through R8, causing the output transistors and the relay to be switched off once again.

D3 is the usual protective diode, and this suppresses the high voltage spike which would otherwise be produced across the relay coil as it de-energised. C1, R2, C10, R9, and C11 are supp decoupling components, and S1 is the on/off switch. SK1 enables the audio output of the receiver to be monitored using a crystal earpiece, and this is extremely helpful when adjusting and aligning the finished receiver.

Construction And Adjustment

Coil L1 is home constructed, and is would on a ¼ inch (6mm) diameter coil former which is fitted with a tuning slug. It consists of precisely 10 turns of 0.9mm diameter (or about 16 SWG) enamelled copper wire, and the turns are closely spaced so that the coil is about 10mm high. Use a coil former which has a horozontal base section which permits the unit to be mounted by means of a couple of 8BA screws and nuts (this is the usual type of ¼ inch former). Then a soldertag can be mounted on each of the mounting bolts, and these act as suitable anchor points for the ends of the winding. C2 can be mounted across these soldertags.

Ideally the receiver should be constructed on a p.c.b. as this will provide a rigid, compact, and reliable assembly. However, plain matrix can also be used provided a generous amount of solder is used on each joint, and this was the constructional form employed on the prototype. 0.15 inch matrix board is the most convenient to use. RC crystals are normally encapsulated in a HC25U type holder, and so the crystal can be mounted in a holder of the same type. It is probably better to solder this component directly into circuit though, in the interest of reliability, but make sure that the joints are made quickly and efficiently so that neither the crystal or its mounting are damaged by heat.

The aerial consists of a piece of PVC covered hook up wire about 1 metre long. It can be somewhat shorter, but this will result in some loss of sensitivity. A telescopic aerial can be used if preferred. In either case the aerial should be mounted vertically, or if this is not practical, it can be mounted at an angle of about 45 degrees.

Alignment of the receiver is very simple as there are only two tuned circuits to adjust. With a crystal earphone connected to SK1 and a working transmitter (modulation on) placed near the receiver, L1 and IFT1 are both adjusted to the peak the received signal. Adjust L1 first, and then adjust the core IFT1 using a proper trimming tool (Denco TT5 or similar).

Then the aerial of the transmitter should be collapsed somewhat and (or) the transmitter should be placed some distance away from the receiver, so that only a fairly weak signal is received. L1 and IFT1 are then accuratley peaked up on this signal.

Note that changes in the length or even just in the orientation of the aerial can make it necessary to repeak the core of L1. Also, leads connecting to the relay must be kept a reasonable distance away from the aerial as the system could otherwise become unstable.

Radio Control Receiver Components

Resistors. All are miniature ¼ or 1/8 watt 5 or 10%.

R1	1k.
R2	120 ohms.
R3	100k.
R4	6.8k (see text).
R5	1k.
R6	1.2 Meg.
R7	4.7k.
R8	100k.
R9	150 ohms.
R10	100k.
R11	100k.

Capacitors

C1	100nf plastic foil or ceramic.
C2	39pf ceramic plate or polystyrene.
C3	10nf plastic foil or ceramic.
C4	10nf plastic foil.
C5	220nf plastic foil.
C6	220nf plastic foil.
C7	820pf ceramic plate.
C8	4.7mfd. 10v.w.
C9	1mfd. 10v.w.
C10	470mfd. 10v.w.
C11	470mfd. 10v.w.
C12	56pf ceramic plate or polystyrene.
C13	8.2pf ceramic plate or polystyrene.
C14	2.2pf ceramic plate.

Semiconductors
Tr1   BF244B.
Tr2   BC109C.
Tr3   2N4062 (any version
Tr4   BC109C
Tr5   BC109C
IC1   ZN414
D1   OA91.
D2   OA91.
D3   1N914

Inductors.
L1   Home made (see text).
IFT1   Denco IFT 13/470kHz.
Relay   6 volt coil, 185 ohms or more, contacts as required.
X1   27mHz band radio control crystal for 470kHz I.F.
         (see text)

Miscellaneous
Miniature SPST toggle switch (S1) Crystal Earpiece 3.5mm
Jack Skt. 9 volt battery etc.

Radio Control Transmitter

The circuit diagram of the transmitter appears in Fig. 10.
This uses the usual MOPA (Master Oscillator Power Amplifier).
arrangement.

Tr1 is used as a crystal controlled Colpitts oscillator of exactly
the same design as the one employed in the receiver. The output from this is fed to a power amplifier and multiplier stage
which uses Tr2. Here the nominal 9MHz output from Tr1 is
multiplied to 27MHz, amplified, and fed to the aerial. The
output stage is a simple Class A type.

IC1 is the popular NE555V timer, and this is used in the astable
mode to provide the audio modulation signal. When S1 is open
circuit the circuit will not oscillate, and the IC will latch with
its output terminal (pin 3) at virtually the full supply rail
potential. Power will thus be supplied to the RF circuitry
and an unmodulated carrier wave will be transmitted.

45

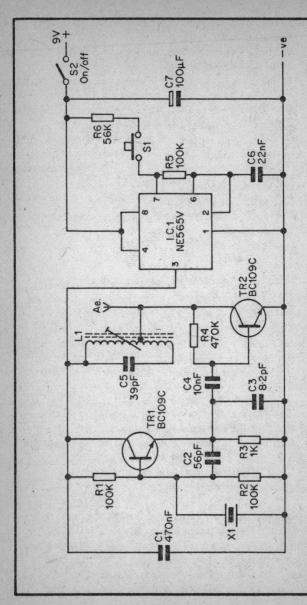

Fig. 10. The circuit diagram of the Radio Control Transmitter.

46

When S1 is operated, the astable circuit is completed and IC1 will begin to oscillate at a frequency of a few hundred Hz. This causes the power to the RF circuitry to be chopped on and off at the same frequency, and so the carrier wave is rather crudely (but adequately for this application) modulated with an audio tone. One problem with this simple arrangement is that the output from IC1 is a high quality squarewave, and it is therefore rich in harmonics. These harmonics must be attenuated as the circuit would otherwise radiate a significant amount of signal outside the RC band. This attenuation is provided by C1, which also acts as an RF decoupling capacitor.

S2 is the on/off switch. The current consumption of the unit is about 15 to 20mA.

Construction And Adjustment

Again, a p.c.b. is probably the best constructional basis for the project, but plain matrix board can be used, and the prototype was constructed on a 0.1 inch matrix board. 0.15 matrix board is unsuitable as it is not compatible with the 0.1inch pin spacing of the NE555V IC. L1 is identical to L1 of the receiver, except that half way up the winding (approximately) the enamel insulation is scaped off a small area of wire, and this point is tinned with solder. This forms the tapping to which Tr2 collector, R4, and the aerial connect. The aerial is a telescopic type, and should be about a metre or so long. The unit can be powered from either a 9 or 12 volt supply, the higher voltage having the advantage of providing a slightly higher output power, and therefore giving better range and reliability.

The only adjustment which must be made to the completed transmitter is to peak L1 for maximum output. This is done by using a field strength monitor to indicate the comparative output from the unit while L1 is simply adjusted for maximum meter deflection. The unit should always be used with the aerial fully extended as this will provide the strongest field strength and the greatest reliability. L1 should be adjusted with

47

the aerial fully extended as changes in the length of the aerial will affect the setting at which L1 peaks the output signal.

Once L1 has been correctly peaked it is advisable to use some wax or adhesive to lock the core in position so that vibration does not cause the core to become detuned. L1 of the receiver should be similarly treated.

Radio Control Transmitter Components

Resistors. All are miniature ¼ watt 5 or 10%.

R1	100k.
R2	100k.
R3	1k.
R4	470k.
R5	100k.
R6	56k.

Capacitors

C1	470nf plastic foil.
C2	56pf ceramic plate or polystyrene.
C3	8.2pf ceramic plate or polystyrene.
C4	10nf plastic foil or ceramic.
C5	39pf ceramic plate or polystyrene.
C6	22nf plastic foil.
C7	100mfd. 10v. w.

Semiconductors

Tr1	BC109C
Tr2	BC109C
IC1	NE555V.

Miscellaneous.

X1	27MHz band radio control crystal to match X1 in the receiver (see text).
L1	Home made, see text for details.

Telescopic aerial about 1 metre or so long when extended. Push to make non-locking push button switch (S1), and SPST toggle switch (S2).
Case, battery, etc.

CHAPTER 2

AUDIO PROJECTS

The subject for the 2nd. Chapter was as easy to choose as
that for the first Chapter, since the field of audio is probably
the only one which seriously rivals radio in terms of popularity. Apart from a couple of amplifiers, including a high
quality unit, several Hi-Fi add-on units will be described as well
as a simple multichannel mixer.

General Purpose Amplifier

This simple design is intended for general purpose use, and it is
an extremely useful piece of equipment to have around. It is
surprising the number of occasions on which an amplifier of
this type can be put to good use. The circuit diagram of the
unit is shown in Fig. 11.

The circuit is based on the popular LM380N IC which has
the advantage over most other ICs of requiring very few discrete
components to complete a practical amplifier. A practical
amplifier can be constructed using this IC and just three
discrete components. These are an output DC blocking
capacitor (C5), an input DC blocking capacitor (C4), and a
supply decoupling capacitor (C1).

There are two drawbacks to using just a basic circuit of this
type in the present application, and these are the inadequate
voltage gain and input impedance of the circuit. The LM380N
has typical input impedance and voltage gain figures of 150k
and 50 respectively. Ideally for this application these should
be about ten times higher in each case, so that the amplifier
could operate from high impedance low level loads, such as a
crystal microphone.

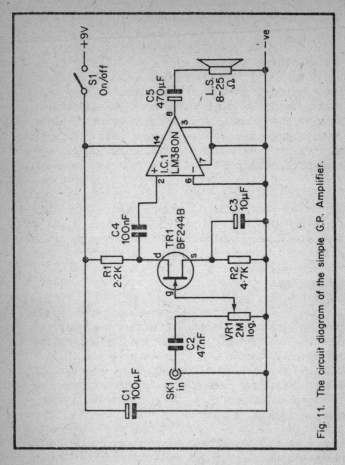

Fig. 11. The circuit diagram of the simple G.P. Amplifier.

Therefore, in order to boost the input impedance and voltage gain of the basic circuit an f.e.t. common source preamplifier stage has been added. This utilizes Tr1. VR1 is the volume control, and this doubles as the gate bias resistor for Tr1. C2 provides DC blocking at the input. S1 is the on/off switch, and this can be ganged with VR1 if desired. C1 is the only supply decoupling capacitor that is required for the entire amplifier circuit.

The unit can feed any speaker having an impedance of 8 ohms or more, and it will produce a maximum output of about 1 watt into an 8 ohm load when used with a fresh battery (which should be a fairly large type such as a PP7 or PP9). With higher impedance loads the maximum output power will be lower than this, and it will also be somewhat less when the battery has aged somewhat, and its internal resistance has increased. The quiescent current consumption of the unit is about 9mA., but the LM380N has a class B output stage, and the current consumption rises to many times this figure at high volume peaks.

The LM380N incorporates both thermal overload and output short circuit protection circuitry, and so it will not be damaged if a speaker of less than 8 ohms impedance is used. It will, however, be rather inefficient with regard to current consumption.

Construction

Although the circuit of this project is very simple and straight-forward, this is rather deceptive in that the unit is quite critical from the constructional viewpoint. This is due to the fact that the circuit has an input impedance of about 2 Meg ohms, and at maximum sensitivity only a few mV. are needed at the input in order to produce maximum output. The circuit has been arranged so that the input and output are out of phase, and any stray feedback between the two will not, there-fore, result in instability. It is still necessary to use screened cable at the input though, in order to prevent stray pick-up of mains hum and other forms of electrical interference. It is also necessary to use a layout that avoids feedback paths through the supply rails, etc.

The layout of this project is probably more critical than that for the radio projects which were featured in the previous Chapter. In order to assist the inexperienced reader a suitable Veroboard (0.1 inch. matrix) layout for the unit is shown in Fig. 12.

51

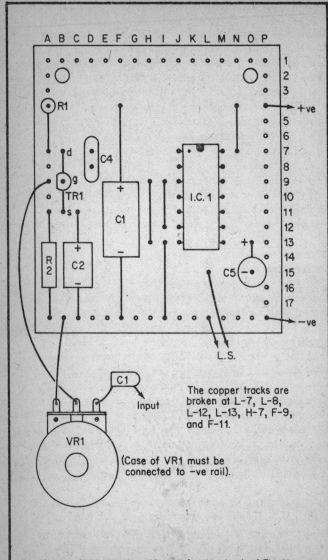

Fig. 12. A suitable Veroboard layout for the circuit of Fig. 11.

52

General Purpose Amplifier Components

Resistors. Both miniature ¼ watt 5 or 10%.
R1   2.2k.
R2   4.7k.
VR1   2 Meg. log. carbon (can be ganged with S1 if
        desired).

Capacitors.
C1   100mfd. 10v.w.
C2   47nf plastic foil.
C3   10mfd. 10v.w.
C4   100nf plastic foil.
C5   470mfd. 6v.w.

Semiconductors.
IC1   LM380N
Tr1   BF244B.

Miscellaneous.
8 to 25 ohms impedance loudspeaker.
SPST toggle switch (S1, see above).
9 volt battery, input socket, case, etc.

10 Watt Audio Amplifier

Probably most people associate the term 'audio' with the
field of Hi-Fi equipment, and all the projects which make up
the rest of this chapter fall into this category.

The first of these is a high quality 10 watt audio amplifier, and
the circuit diagram of this unit is shown in Fig. 13. It can be
used in conjunction with other projects described in this book
to produce a complete 10 watt plus 10 watt stereo amplifier.

The circuit of the amplifier is very straightforward, and is
quite conventional. Tr4 and Tr5 are the complementary
emitter follower output stage, Tr2 is the common emitter
driver stage, and Tr1 is the common emitter input stage. The
emitter of Tr1 couples to the emitters of Tr4 and Tr5, and so

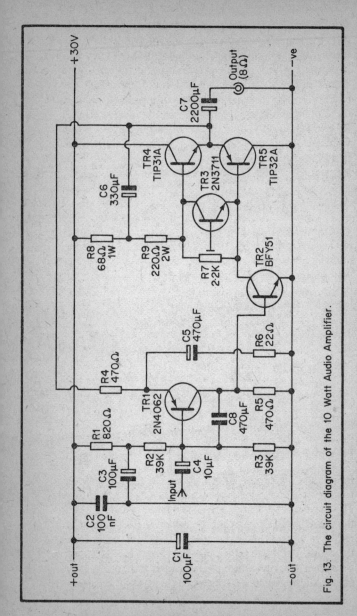

Fig. 13. The circuit diagram of the 10 Watt Audio Amplifier.

54

there is virtually a 100% negative feedback loop here. This gives the amplifier a voltage gain of almost exactly unity. By biasing the base of Tr1 to about half the supply rail potential, the output of the amplifier assumes about the same potential. This is, of course, what is required in order to enable the circuit to produce the maximum output voltage swing, and therefore the maximum unclipped output power also. R2 and R3 bias the input of the amplifier, and R1 plus C3 form a decoupling network which attenuate any hum or noise on the supply lines which would otherwise be coupled to the input of the circuit. C1 and C2 are supply decoupling capacitors.

At audio frequencies some of the negative feedback is decoupled by C5, and R6 limits the amount of feedback which is removed. This limiting is used as the full voltage gain of the circuit is not required, and the remaining negative feedback reduces the noise and distortion levels of the amplifier. Theoretically the voltage gain of the amplifier is roughly equal to R4 divided by R6, although in practice the gain is less than this due to losses in the output transistors.

Tr3 is used as an amplified diode, and its purpose is to provide a small forward bias to the output transistors. This bias is needed in order to compensate for the 600mV. or so that is needed at the base of each output transistor before it will begin to turn on. Without this bias severe crossover distortion would occur. This is one of the most objectionable forms of distortion, this mainly being due to the fact that it occurs most strongly on low level signals, and because it is on such signals that distortion is most noticeable.

In practice Tr3 should be positioned close to the output transistors, and it will then help to prevent thermal runaway. This is where the output transistors heat up slightly due to the fairly heavy output currents which they handle, which results in an increase in the quiescent output current which they pass. This increase is caused by the reduction in the base — emitter turn on voltage of the output transistors, (which affects all bipolar transistors when they are subjected to an increase in temperature). This increase in temperature will increase the temperature inside the case of the amplifier, and thus it will be transfered to Tr3. This will cause a reduction in the base – emitter turn on voltages of Tr3, which will result in a fall in the voltage developed across its collector–emitter terminals. This reduces the forward bias to the output transistors, and so compensates for the original increase in output current.

C4 provides DC blocking at the input, and C7 provides the same function at the output. C6 is the usual bootstrapping capacitor, and this increases the maximum output voltage swing which can be achieved by the circuit. C8 provides high frequency roll off, and this helps to prevent instability due to stray feedback, and also minimises the risk of radio interference breaking through.

Construction

The input impedance of the circuit is not very high, being something in the order of 10k or so. Neither is the input sensitivity particularly high, with about 450mV. RMS being needed to produce full output. This makes the layout of the unit not very critical, but one or two points must be borne in mind.

Under full output conditions a supply current of about 500mA. or so flows in the power supply and output wiring. This can result in small but significant voltages being developed in the relevant wiring, with unwanted feedback being produced as a result of this. Use connecting wire of an adequate guage (7 x 0.2mm or thicker), and do not connect the negative supply rail to the amplifier via one of the speaker connections. These should both connect to the amplifier board close to Tr5 collector.

Tr4 and Tr5 should be given as much heatsinking as possible. If the amplifier has a metal case or chassis it will probably be satisfactory to use this as the heatsink. It is usually inconvenient to bolt output transistors directly to a case unless they are mounted away from the rest of the circuit, which is not advisable as there would then be a poor thermal contact between the output transistors and Tr3. It is probably better to use the method outlined in Fig. 14. If it is not feasible to use the case or chassis as a heatsink, a large type commercial heatsink can be used. Small vaned type heatsinks are available for this type of transistor, but it is unlikely that such a heatsink would prove to be adequate for this purpose.

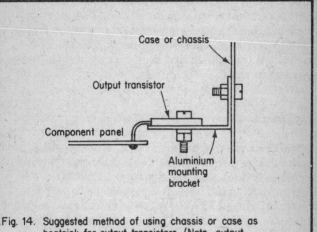

Fig. 14. Suggested method of using chassis or case as heatsink for output transistors. (Note, output transistors must be insulated from mounting bracket in the usual way).

Tr2 must also be fitted with a heatsink, and a small clip-on type will just about suffice. However, it is preferable to use a panel mounting type TO5 heatsink, and then connect this to a small fin of about 16 SWG aluminium. In either case Tr2 will run at quite a high temperature (it will be too hot to touch).

Before connecting the finished amplifier to a power supply it is essential that R7 is adjusted for minimum resistance between the base and collector of Tr3. A multimeter set to read something in the region of 100mA. f.s.d. should be used to monitor the current consumption of the unit when it is first connected to the supply. A quiescent current of about 50 to 60mA. should flow. By adjusting R7 it should be possible to find a setting at which this current is greatly increased with any slight advance in the setting of R3. R7 can either be left at this threshold setting, or slightly advanced from it in order to produce an increase in the current consumption of about 2 or 3mA.

It should perhaps be explained that this is not providing a sufficiently large bias to the output transistor to eliminate crossover distortion, but such distortion will not be evident as the circuit employs quite a large amount of negative feedback which will reduce this distortion to an insignificant level. If preferred, R7 can be adjusted to produce a slightly higher quiescent current in the output transistors, but this current should not be more than about 15mA.

The circuit should not be employed with a supply voltage of more than 30 volts, and in order to obtain the specified output power the supply voltage should not be much less than 30 volts under full load (about 1 Amp. or so). This makes it virtually a necessity to use a stabilised supply, and a suitable unit is described later in this book. It is possible to use a supply voltage of less than 30 volts, but this will result in a reduction in the maximum available output power. Similarly, using a speaker having an impedance of more than 8 ohms will produce a reduced output power. Of course, only a single amplifier is shown in the circuit diagram on Fig. 13, and two such units must be constructed for use in a stereo amplifier, which it is assumed most constructors will do. Note that if the amplifier is constructed as a mono unit the maximum current consumption will only be about 50mA. or so.

Performance

There will inevitably be some variation in performance between individual amplifiers built to this design, but simple

mplifiers of this type offer quite a high level of performance.
The total harmonic distortion level is typically less than 0.2%
t power levels up to 100 Watts rms. The -3dB. points are at
bout 20Hz and 60kHz, and the unweighted signal to noise
atio is about -80dB. (assuming a well smoothed supply is used).

10 Watt Amplifier Components

Resistors. Miniature ¼ watt 5 or 10% except where noted
otherwise.

R1	820 ohms.
R2	39k.
R3	39k.
R4	470 ohms.
R5	470 ohms.
R6	22 ohms.
R7	2.2k preset.
R8	68 ohms 1 Watt.
R9	220 ohms 2 Watt.

Capacitors.

C1	100mfd. 40v.w.
C2	100nf plastic foil.
C3	100mfd. 40v.w.
C4	10mfd. 25v.w.
C5	470mfd. 25v.w.
C6	330mfd. 16v.w.
C7	2200mfd. 25v.w.

Semiconductors.

Tr1	2N4062 (any version)
Tr2	BFY51.
Tr3	2N3711.
Tr4	TIP31A.
Tr5	TIP32A.

Miscellaneous.
Insulating sets for output transistors.
Heatsink, componet panel, etc.
Note that two sets of components are required for a stereo
amplifier).

Preamplifier/Tone Controls

This circuit, which is shown in Fig. 15, is primarily intended for use with the power amplifier just described in the previous section. By using two of these amplifiers in conjunction with two preamplifier/tone control circuits it is possible to produce a good quality stereo amplifier having inputs for ceramic or crystal cartridge, tape deck, and tuner. The ceramic/crystal cartridge input can, if required, be converted to a magnetic cartridge input by adding the preamplifier described in the next part of this Chapter.

Tr1 is used as the basis of the preamplifier, and this must perform two functions. It must raise the input impedance of the basic circuit to a level of about 1 Meg. so that the circuit will perform satisfactorily with a crystal or ceramic cartridge. It must also provide a certain amount of voltage gain in order to compensate for the losses in the passive tone control networks which are used. Tr1 is a Jugfet which is used in the common source mode, and it provides a voltage gain of a little over 20dB. (ten times). VR1 is the volume control and this also acts as the gate bias resistance for Tr1. The gain of the pre-amplifier slightly more than compensates for the losses in the tone controls, and this raises the input sensitivity of the amplifier to about 350mV. rms for maximum output. This is sufficient for use with most tuners, pick-ups, and tape decks.

The tone controls are passive types of conventional design. Although many people believe that passive tone control circuits provide more limited control than active types this is not in fact the case. Passive circuits are capable of the same degree of control as a similar active design. The controls in this design provide approximately 12dB. of boost and cut at 100Hz and 10kHz with reference to 1kHz. VR2 is the bass control and VR3 is the treble control.

VR4 is the balance control, and can, of course, be omitted if a mono version of the amplifier is being constructed. Note that unlike the other components in the circuit, this does not

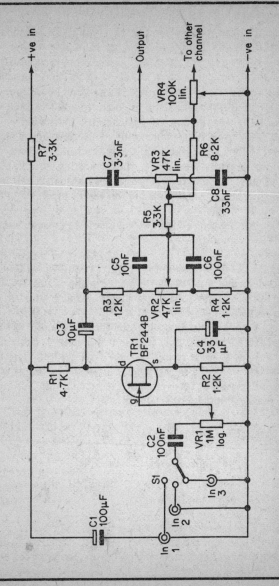

Fig. 15. The circuit diagram of the Preamplifier/Tone controls.

61

have to be duplicated in the other channel of a stereo amplifier as it is common to both channels.

Construction

The preamplifier can be constructed using Vereoboard, a p.c.b., etc., but it is advisable to use point to point wiring when constructing the tone control circuitry. Otherwise there is likely to be a large number of connecting wires which will tend to look untidy, pick up mains hum, and can easily lead to wiring errors being made. The connecting wires in the input circuitry must all be screened as the impedance here is quite high at about 1 Megohm, and this results in a high susceptibility to pick up of mains hum. Neither the pre-amplifier nor the tone control wiring should be close to the power supply circuitry.

Adding the preamplifier and tone control circuits must result in some degradation of the performance of the circuit as a whole, but the overall level of total harmonic distortion should still be only about 0.5% or less at any output power level. Provided the input wiring is adequately screened and a reasonably smoothed power supply is used, it should be possible to obtain a signal to noise ratio of about -70dB. With the tone controls adjusted for a flat response the frequency response of the amplifier will not be significantly affected by the addition of the preamplifier and tone controls.

Preamplifier/Tone Controls Components

Resistors. All are miniature ¼ watt 5 or 10%.
R1   4.7k.
R2   1.2k.
R3   12k.
R4   1.2k.
R5   3.3k.
R6   8.2k.
R7   3.3k.

R1   1 Meg. log. carbon.
R2   47k lin. carbon.
R3   47k lin. carbon.
R4   100k lin. carbon.

apacitors.
1   100mfd. 40v.w.
2   100nf plastic foil.
3   10mfd. 25v.w.
4   33mfd. 10.w.v.
5   10nf plastic foil.
6   100nf plastic foil.
7   3.3nf plastic foil.
8   33nf plastic foil.

emiconductor.
r1   BF244B.

iscellaneous.
way 4 pole rotary switch (only one pole used, or two for a
ereo version).
put sockets, component panel, etc.
Note that for stereo two sets of components are required
xcept for S1 and the potentiometers. VR1, VR2, and VR3
ould be dual gang types for a stereo unit).

agnetic Cartridge Preamplifier

though designed for use with the amplifier system just
scribed, this circuit can be used as a ceramic to magnetic
put converter for any amplifier which only has provision for
ceramic or crystal type cartridge. The circuit diagram of the
agnetic cartridge preamplifier appears in Fig. 16.

en using a crystal or ceramic cartridge it is possible to
tain a flat frequency response merely by operating the
vice into a fairly high impedance (usually about 1 Meg ohm).
e output from a crystal or ceramic cartridge is also high,
d is usually something in the region of 1 volt peak to peak.
magnetic cartridge has very different properties, and cannot
used successfully using direct connection to a crystal or
mic pick-up input.

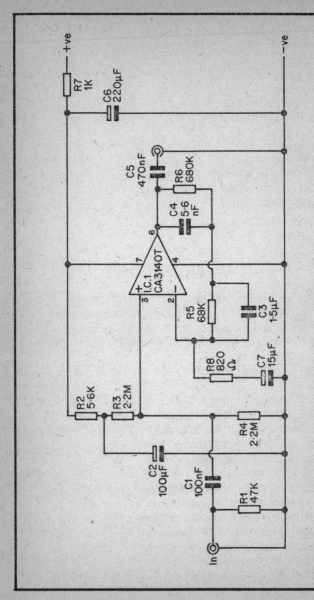

Fig. 16. The circuit diagram of the magnetic cartridge preamplifier.

64

Most magnetic pick-ups are designed to match into a medium impedance input, the actual figure almost invariably being 47k. They provide only a comparatively low output signal, perhaps as little as 10mV. peak to peak at 1kHz. The output level is not flat over the entire audio spectrum, but is higher at treble frequencies and lower at bass ones. Strictly speaking this output characteristic is not the fault of the cartridge, but is due to the fact that bass cut and treble boost are supplied to the audio signal which is fed to the cutting head. The purpose of the treble boost is to enable a flat frequency response to be obtained when a similar degree of treble cut is applied at the playback equipment. This produces an improved signal to noise ratio. The bass cut is necessary in order to ensure that excessively large groove modulation does not occur on high level bass signals, as groove wall collapse could be produced by such excessive modulation.

To summarize then: a magnetic cartridge preamplifier must provide an input impedance of 47k, a fairly high level of voltage gain, and frequency response shaping (or equalization as it is often termed).

The circuit uses a single IC (per channel), and the IC actually used is the CA3140T operational amplifier. An advantage of this IC over most other types is that it can provide an output voltage swing which is virtually equal to the supply potential, and this gives it the highest possible input overload margin. When used with a 30 volt supply rail the overload margin is more than 26dB.

The IC is used in the non-inverting mode, and the non-inverting input of the device is biased by R3 and R4. R2 and C2 filter out any noise on the supply line which would otherwise be fed to the non-inverting input via R3. R5 and R6 bias the inverting input, and together with C3, C4, R8, and C7, they set the voltage gain of the amplifier and provide the equalisation. At middle frequencies the gain of the circuit is a little under 40dB., and so about 4mV. is required at the input in order to produce full output from the power amplifiers (with the volume control adjusted for maximum sensitivity).

R1 is used to shunt the input of the circuit and so reduce the basic input impedance of the circuit (which is about 1.1 Meg.) to the required level of 47k. C1 provides DC blocking at the input. At first sight it might seem to be easier simply to omit R1, raise the value of C1, and then reduce the values of R3 and R4 to provide the required input impedance. The disadvantage of this system is that it results in a significant surge current being passed through the cartridge at switch on and switch off, which is not desirable. Another advantage of this system is that it is easy to alter the input impedance to suit pick-ups which require an input impedance of other than 47k. For instance, some types require a load impedance of 100k, and an input impedance of approximately this level can be achieved by altering the value of R1 to 100k.

C5 provides DC blocking at the output, and C6 plus R7 provide supply decoupling.

Construction

Although the input and output of the circuit are in phase, and the circuit has a fairly high voltage gain and input impedance, stray pick up between the output and input is unlikely to cause any problems with instability. The reason for this is simply that the equalization circuitry results in the high frequency response of the circuit being greatly attenuated, and it is only at these frequencies that significant stray pick up could occur. However, the equalization results in a considerable bass boost being applied to the circuit, and this coupled with the fact that the circuit is very sensitive anyway, means that screened leads must be used at the input, and unscreened wires (component leadouts, etc.) must be kept as short as possible, as otherwise there will be a significant breakthrough of mains hum. Apart from this the method of construction and layout is not particularly critical.

A common problem when using a magnetic cartridge is that of hum loops. This is where a loud hum is produced from the output, sometimes accompanied by an apparent lack of gain, and the cause is not stray pick up in the input wiring. In a severe case the amplifier can even begin to oscillate. The cause of hum loops and feedback loops is badly arranged earthing. The general rule here is to make sure that each part of the circuit (including the cartridge) is earthed, but only once. For example, hum loops are often caused by the deck and cartridge being earthed at both the amplifier and the mains earth of the deck. The cure is to not earth the pick up at the mains earth of the deck.

If the circuit is to be constructed as a self contained add-on unit for an existing amplifier, then it can be powered from a small 9 volt battery such as a PP3. R7 can then be omitted, with the supply being connected straight across C6. A mains power unit can be used if prefered, and again R7 can be omitted. The supply voltage should not be allowed to exceed 36 volts, which is the maximum permissable supply voltage for the CA3140T. In order to give the circuit a reasonably good overload margin it is preferable not to use a nominal supply voltage of less than 9 volts, although the CA3140T will operate satisfactorily with a supply voltage as low as 4 volts.

Magnetic Cartridge Preamplifier Components

Resistors. All miniature ¼ watt 5 or 10%.

R1	47k.
R2	5.6k.
R3	2.2 Meg.
R4	2.2 Meg.
R5	68k.
R6	680k.
R7	1k.
R8	820 ohms.

Capacitors
C1	100nf plastic foil.
C2	100mfd. 40v.w.
C3	1.5nf plastic foil.
C4	5.6nf plastic foil.

C5   470nf plastic foil.
C6   220mfd. 40v.w.
C7   15mfd. 25v.w.

Semiconductor
IC1   CA3140T

Miscellaneous
Input socket, component panel, etc.
(Note that for stereo operation two sets of components are required).

Dynamic Noise Filter

The main problem when playing an inexpensive cassette deck or an ordinary cassette recorder through a Hi-Fi system is the relatively high background noise level which is produced. This tape hiss, as it is generally termed, covers the entire audio frequency spectrum, but it is the high frequency content which is most noticeable. Thus it is possible to greatly reduce the noise (or to apparently do so at any rate) by backing off the treble control, which is probably what most users of this type of equipment do.

At high signal levels the tape hiss becomes unnoticeable as it is masked by the main signal, even if the high frequencies are not attenuated. This enables an effective noise reduction system to be produced by using a treble cut filter which only operates on fairly low level signals. The treble cut then reduces noise on low level signals, where it would otherwise be very prominent, without any loss of treble response being incurred at high signal levels.

It is on this basic principle that dynamic noise filters operate. In order to be really effective such units have to have one slight refinement in that they must be made to respond to the level of the high frequency content on the signal which is being processed, rather than to the general signal level. This is because high frequency signals will more readily mask the tape hiss than will bass or middle frequencies. Thus, without this refinement the tape hiss would be heard to come and go as certain types of signal were handled, and it could also lead to a more subtle problem known as breathing effects (which is largely self explanatory).

The complete circuit diagram of the dynamic noise filter is shown in Fig. 17. The input signal is slit into three parts, with most of the signal being coupled via C6 to one input of a simple passive mixer circuit which uses R9 and R10. The second part of the signal is fed to a simple high pass filter which is comprised of C5 and R5, and from here the signal is applied to a unity gain inverting amplifier. The output from this is applied to the second input of the passive mixer.

As the two signals which are applied to the mixer are 180 degrees out of phase they have a cancelling effect on one another. However, only high frequencies are applied to the second input of the mixer, and so only the treble frequencies are cancelled out. The circuit thus provides treble cut.

Tr4 is used as a low gain, common emitter amplifier, and this acts as a buffer between the mixer and the output, and it also compensates for the losses in the mixer circuit.

The third part of the signal is taken to a simple variable attenuator of the volume control type (R4), and then it is taken to the input of a high gain, common emitter amplifier, which utilizes Tr1. The output from this amplifier is used to drive a diode pump circuit which uses D1 and D2. The positive output voltage of this network is developed across C3 where it is smoothed to produce DC signal. There is a fairly short time constant here though, so that this voltage will rapidly respond to changes in input level. C1 is given a fairly low value so that the circuit only handles high frequency signals.

Tr2 is a Jugfet which is used as a voltage controlled resistor. Under quiescent condition R3 is adjusted to provide a reverse bias to Tr2, so that it exhibits a fairly high resistance.

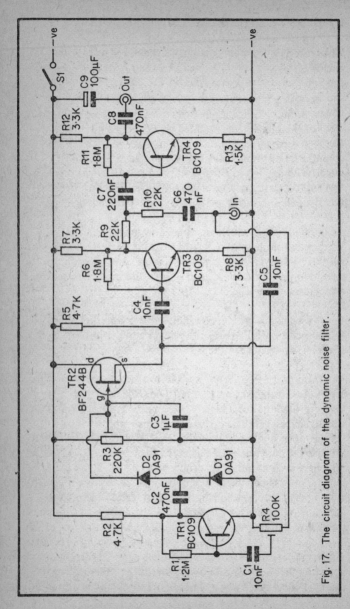

Fig. 17. The circuit diagram of the dynamic noise filter.

70

It then has no significant effect on the circuit.

When a high level, high frequency signal is applied to the circuit a strong bias voltage will be developed across C3, and this will reduce the reverse bias on Tr2, and cause its drain to source resistance to fall to quite a low level, perhaps less than one hundred ohms. The signal via C5 is then virtually short circuited to the positive supply rail, and no significant amount of signal is fed to the second input of the mixer circuit. Therefore, in the absence of a high level, high frequency, signal the circuit applies treble cut to the processed signal, but in the presence of such signals the high frequency attentuation is virtually eliminated. The dynamic noise filter action is thus provided by the circuit.

Adjustment And Use

The circuit has almost unity voltage gain, and it can therefore be connected between the output of the cassette deck or recorder and the input of the amplifier without generating any signal level mismatch. Because the circuit has only unity gain the component layout and method of construction are not all critical. Also, it means that the signal handling stages can use large amounts of negative feedback, so that the circuit introduces no significant amounts of noise and distortion. The circuit will operate with input signal levels from only about 100mV peak to peak up to a few volts peak to peak, and it should therefore be compatible with virtually any system. It is advisable to use screened connecting cables to connect the unit to the cassette deck and amplifier.

When initially adjusting the unit a blank cassette should be played through the system. R3 should be adjusted so that its slider is virtually at the end of the track which connects to the positive supply rail. R4 should be adjusted for minimum output (its slider connected to the negative supply rail). By adjusting the slider of R3 down towards the other end of its track, at some point a drop in the pitch of the noise produced

71

from the speaker should be apparent. The slider of R3 is adjusted just far enough down the track to produce this drop in pitch, and no farther.

A recording is then played through the system, and R4 can be tried at various settings. If it is adjusted for too great an output the tape noise will be heard to accompany fairly low level treble signals. On the other hand, if it is backed off too far the DNL action will be virtually non-existent. With a little trial and error it should be possible to locate a good compromise setting without too much trouble.

Dynamic Noise Filter Components

Resistors. All are miniature ¼ watt 5 or 10%.

R1   1.2 Meg.
R2   4.7k.
R3   220k preset.
R4   100k preset.
R5   4.7k
R6   1.8 Meg.
R7   3.3k.
R8   3.3k.
R9   22k.
R10 22k.
R11 1.8 Meg.
R12 3.3k.
R13 1.5k.

Capacitors.
C1   10nf plastic foil.
C2   470nf plastic foil.
C3   1mfd. plastic foil.
C4   10nf plastic foil.
C5   10nf plastic foil.
C6   470nf plastic foil.
C7   220nf plastic foil.
C8   470nf plastic foil.
C9   100mfd. 10v.w.

Semiconductors.
Tr1   BC109.
Tr2   BF244B.
Tr3   BC109.
Tr4   BC109.
D1   OA91.
D2 • OA91.

Miscellaneous.
SPST toggle switch (S1)
Input and output sockets, 9 volt battery, component panel, etc.

Rumble Filter

Although the highest quality records and record decks currently
available are capable of almost perfect results, cheaper record
decks and some records produce quite significant amounts
of rumble. Much of this noise is just below the lower limits of
human hearing, but it can still produce audible effects due to
cross modulation (or intermodulation distortion as it is also
termed) with the wanted signal. The amount of rumble within
the audible range can sometimes be at a sufficient level to be
quite distracting.

A rumble filter is merely a circuit which rolls off frequencies
below 100Hz (approximately) at a fairly high rate, and thus
greatly alleviates the problems associated with an excessively
high rumble level. The circuit diagram of a simple rumble
filter is shown in Fig. 18.

This uses a combination of a conventional active high pass
filter and a simple passive high pass filter. IC1 is used as a
non-inverting amplifier, and it has unity voltage gain as there
is a 100% negative feedback loop between the output and the
inverting input. R1 and R3 provide the bias voltage for the
non-inverting input of the IC.

The value of C3 is chosen to roll-off the unwanted frequencies
by acting as a simple R/C filter in conjunction with R1 and

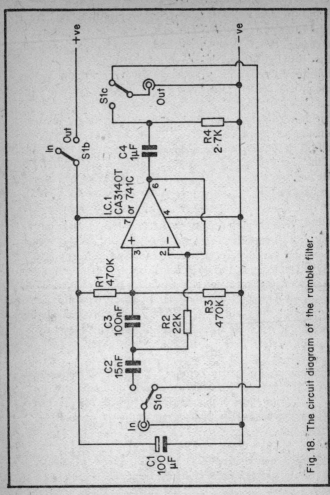

Fig. 18. The circuit diagram of the rumble filter.

R3. At fairly high frequencies R2 will have no significant effect on the circuit as it will appear to have an infinite impedance. This is because any change in voltage at its input end will be matched by a similar change at the output end, due to the fact that the amplifier has unity gain and is non-invertin At low frequencies the circuit does not achieve unity gain due

74

o the attenuation provided by C3, R1, and R3. R2 therefore exhibits some impedance (although not as low as its actual impedance) to the input signal, and forms a second high pass filter in conjunction with C2. This gives the circuit a roll-off rate of about 12dB. per octave, which is about double the rate provided by a simple passive R — C high pass filter.

One drawback of this type of circuit is that a small peak often occurs in the response just above the point where the roll off commences. This can be tamed by suitable adjustment of the component values, but this results in a reduction in the attenuation rate. Instead, in this case an R/C high pass filter has been added at the output, and this eliminates the peak in the response, and increases the roll-off rate of the circuit. This additional filtering is provided by C4 and R4.

The relevant part of the circuit's frequency response is shown in Fig. 19. This shows the output level (with an input of 1,000mV.) versus frequency.

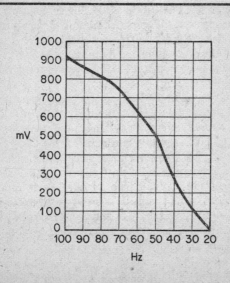

Fig. 19.

S1 is the "in/out" switch, and in the "out" position this disconnects the input and output sockets from the filter circuitry, and connects the two sockets directly together. It also cuts the positive supply line to the filter.

Construction

As the circuit has only unity voltage gain and is designed to operate in a fairly high level part of the system, construction is not particularly critical. However, input and output leads should be screened in order to avoid stray pick-up.

The circuit is designed for connection between the pre-amplifier and the power amplifier stages, and most amplifiers have either a pre-out/main-in facility, or a tape monitoring facility which can be used here. The circuit has a fairly high input impedance and so it can be used between a crystal or ceramic pick-up and the amplifier input. If a 47k resistor is connected across the input it can also be used between a magnetic cartridge and the amplifier input, although this may result in a noticeable reduction in the signal to noise ratio of the system as any noise generated by the circuit will be subjected to the full amplification of the rest of the system.

If a CA3140T is used in the IC1 position it will be possible to power the unit from a 9 volt battery supply. A mains unit providing an output voltage of anything in the range 9 to 36 volts (the latter is the absolute maximum for the CA3140T) can also be used. The 741C will not provide such a high peak to peak output voltage swing as the CA3140T for any given supply voltage, and so it could be overloaded if run from a supply voltage as low as 9 volts. It is therefore advisable to power the circuit from a supply of between 15 and 36 volts if the 741C is employed in the circuit. Performance will otherwise be much the same whichever IC is used.

The circuit should not be operated into a load impedance of less than about 20k, as otherwise the load impedance will

shunt R5 and cause an excessive reduction of low frequencies.
Note that some inexpensive record decks produce a significant
amount of rumble at comparatively high frequencies, and a
filter of this type may be of little benefit when used with
such a deck.

Rumble Filter Components

Resistors. All are miniature ¼ watt 5 or 10%.

R1   470k.
R2   22k.
R3   470k.
R4   2.7k.

Capacitors.

C1   100mfd. 10v.w.
C2   15nf plastic foil.
C3   100nf plastic foil.
C4   1mfd. plastic foil.

Semiconductor.

IC1   CA3140T or 741C (see text).

Miscellaneous

Two way three pole switch (S1).

9 volt battery, input and output sockets, etc.

Scratch Filter

Records probably offer a higher level of performance than
any other medium currently in general use, but they suffer
from the disadvantage of being relatively easily damaged. Also,
it is difficult to prevent dust from finding its way into the
grooves, and to remove it once it has accumulated there. This
results in the familiar background crackling and popping that
often accompanies the playing of a record.

There is no easy way to completely eliminate these noises,
but they can be greatly attenuated by the use of a top cut
filter having a rapid roll-off rate above 6kHz, as most of the
frequencies produced by small record scratches and dust

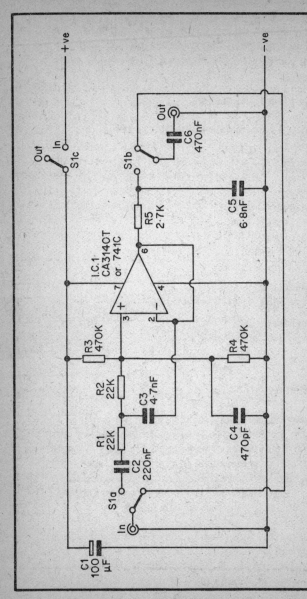

Fig. 20. The circuit diagram of the scratch filter.

78

particles in the grooves are above this frequency. Do not expect a dramatic improvement on noise caused by large dust particles or wide scratches, as these often produce significant amounts of middle and even bass frequencies.

The circuit diagram of a simple scratch filter is shown in Fig.20, and this is really just the low pass equivalent of the high pass filter circuit of Fig. 16. IC1 is used as a unity gain non-inverting amplifier which is biased by R3 and R4. R2 and C4 form a simple R/C low pass filter which reduces the gain of the circuit to less than unity at high frequencies. At low and middle frequencies C3 has an apparent infinite impedance, but at high frequencies it will offer a significant impedance (although R/C still less than its real impedance), and will form a second R/C low pass filter in conjunction with R1. C2 merely provides DC blocking at the input.

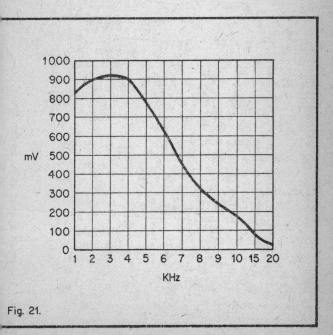

Fig. 21.

In order to speed up the nominal 12dB. per octave roll-off rate of the circuit, and to tame the peak in the response which is produced just below the corner frequency, R/C top cut filter consisting of R5 and C6 is used at the output. C6 provides DC blocking at the output, and S1 is the combined in/out and on/off switch.

The performance of the filter is shown in the graph which appears in Fig. 21.

As far as construction and using the filter are concerned, the notes on the rumble filter, in the main, apply here as well.

Scratch Filter Components

Resistors. All are miniature ¼ watt 5 or 10%.
R1   22k.
R2   22k.
R3   470k.
R4   470k.
R5   2.7k.

Capacitors.
C1   100mfd. 10v.w.
C2   220nf plastic foil.
C3   4.7nf plastic foil.
C4   470pf plastic foil.
C5   6.8nf plastic foil.
C6   470nf plastic foil.

Semiconductor.
IC1   CA3140T or 741C (see text).

Miscellaneous.
Two way three pole switch (S1).
9 volt battery, input and output sockets, etc.

4 Channel Mixer

Mixers are usually associated with the production of tape recordings, but they also find use in the fields of electronic music and disco systems, and probably others as well. The circuit diagram of a simple 4 channel mixer is shown in Fig. 22.

This is based on IC1 which is used as an inverting amplifier. It has its non-inverting input biased by R5 and R6, and by-passed to earth via C6. If we only consider input 1 for the time being: VR1 is the gain control and C2 provides input DC blocking. R1 and R7 set the gain of the amplifier at a little over two times, the actual figure being equal to R7 divided by R1. This is achieved using the virtual earth input system.

IC1 is a differential amplifier, which means that the output voltage is equal to the voltage across the inputs multiplied by the voltage gain of the IC. As this voltage gain is typically something in the region of 200,000 times, only a very small input voltage is needed to tend the output fully positive or fully negative. The output goes positive when the non-inverting (+) input is at a higher potential than the inverting (−) one, and negative if they are the other way round. In this circuit the non-inverting input is biased to about half the supply rail potential, and the inverting input is coupled to the output via R7. Therefore the output must assume the same voltage as that present at the non-inverting input, so that the inverting and non-inverting inputs are at the same potential, and the circuit is balanced.

If an input voltage than takes the left hand end of R1 1 volt positive, for example, in order to maintain the balance of the circuit the output will need to swing a little over two volts negative. By a simple potential divider action the two inputs will then be at the same potential once again. Thus the gain of the circuit is set at just over two times by the ratio of R7 to R1.

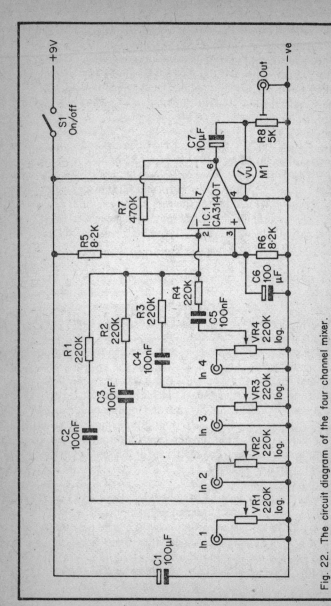

Fig. 22. The circuit diagram of the four channel mixer.

82

Of course, there are four inputs to this circuit, each with its own gain control, DC blocking capacitor, and input resistor. When a circuit of this type has more than one input it acts as a sort of current adder. For instance, if inputs 1, 2, and 3 are taken 1 volt positive, and input 4 is taken 2 volts negative. the current flowing through R4 will cancel out the current through inputs 1 and 2. The output will then have to go a little more than 2 volts negative to cancel out the current through R3 and so balance the circuit. If each input were to be taken (say) 0.5 volts negative, then the output would have to go a little more than 4 volts positive in order to balance the circuit. $(1 + 1 + 1 = 3; 3 - 2 = 1; 1 \times 2 = 2; \frac{1}{2} + \frac{1}{2} + \frac{1}{2} + \frac{1}{2} = 2; 2 \times 2 = 4)$.

Operational amplifiers such as the CA3140T were originally developed to perform mathematical operations in this way, and it is from this that they derive their name. However, this type of circuit is obviously ideal for numerous other functions, including the present one.

C7 provides DC blocking at the output, and R8 is the output level control. M1 is a VU (volume units) meter, and this must be a type which incorporates an integral series resistor and rectifier circuit. The author used one of the popular 60 x 40mm moving coil panel meters. This requires about 1.2 volts rms to produce a reading of OVU, and so the minimum input level for OVU is approximately 500mV. rms. The nominal output level can be anything from 0 to 1.2 volts rms, and is set by R8.

Although the unit is shown here as a four channel mono unit, it can be modified for fewer or more inputs simply by omitting or adding input circuits. For stereo operation two units must be constructed. The unit is intended to accept high level inputs, such as the output from a tape recorder or a tone generator, but it can be modified to operate with low level inputs by adding suitable preamplifiers. For example, input 1 could be made to accept the output from a magnetic cartridge by adding the circuit of Fig. 16 ahead of VR1.

As the circuit has only a low voltage gain and inverts the input signal, the layout of the circuit is not too critical and any normal method should be satisfactory. The input impedance of the circuit is quite high at a little over 100k, and so screened cables should be used here. The noise and distortion produced by the circuit are negligible, and its frequency response is virtually flat over the audio frequency range.

4 Channel Mixer Components

Resistors. All are miniature ¼ watt 5 or 10%.
R1   220k.
R2   220k.
R3   220k.
R4   220k.
R5   8.2k.
R6   8.2k.
R7   470k.
R8   5k (or 4.7k) preset.
VR1 220k. log. carbon.
VR2 220k log. carbon.
VR3 220k. log. carbon.
VR4 220k. log. carbon.

Capacitors.
C1   100mfd. 10.vw.
C2   100nf plastic foil.
C3   100nf plastic foil.
C4   100nf plastic foil.
C5   100nf plastic foil.
C6   100mfd. 6v.w.
C7   10mfd. 10v.w.

Semiconductor.
IC1   CA314OT.

Miscellaneous.
60 x 45 m.m. VU meter with integral rectifier (M1).
SPST toggle switch (S1).
9 volt battery, input and output sockets.

CHAPTER 3

HOUSEHOLD PROJECTS

This Chapter covers a number of projects of the type that are of general use in and around the house, but excluding circuits of the type covered in the previous chapters.

Intercom

This is one of the most useful of all electronic projects, and is possibly the most popular of all electronic projects. The circuit diagram of a simple two station intercom is shown in Fig. 23.

In common with most circuits for this type of equipment, the loudspeaker at each station also doubles as a sort of moving coil microphone in the send mode. In order to obtain a reasonably good frequency response from the microphone it is necessary for the input impedance of the amplifier to be roughly equal to the impedance of the speaker. A common base input stage is therefore used, and this employs Tr1. This provides an input impedance of about 8 ohms, and so the circuit is compatible with 8 ohm speakers, this being the most common impedance for miniature speakers. C2 provides DC blocking at the input, and C3 provides RF filtering. This is necessary as there will obviously be a long connecting cable between the two stations, and this cable will tend to act as a sort of long wire aerial. This can lead to breakthrough of strong radio transmissions, as well as interference caused by refrigerator thermostats, etc., unless remedial measures are taken.

The output from Tr1 collector is coupled to the IC output stage by C5. The output stage uses the LM380N IC in the non-inverting mode. The inverting input is connected to the negative supply rail so as to avoid unwanted stray pick up. The

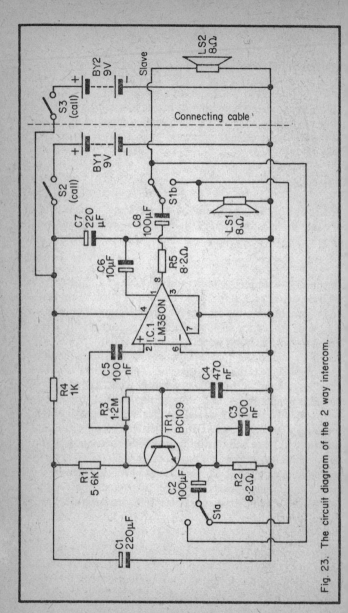

Fig. 23. The circuit diagram of the 2 way intercom.

86

output of the LM380N when operated from a 9 volt supply is sufficient to considerably overload most miniature speakers, and so R5 is connected in series with the output of the circuit in order to limit the output power to a safe maximum level. In the author's experience speakers of about 2½ inches (65mm) in diameter provide the best results. Larger speakers often give a poor treble response when used as microphones, and smaller speakers have both poor efficiency and noticeable lack of bass response. The circuit produces little noise or distortion, and the main limitation on the quality of the system is the speaker/microphones. Small speakers will obviously not provide Hi-Fi quality, and when used as microphones they are far from perfect. Therefore, do not expect too much as far as output quality is concerned, although results on speech should be perfectly acceptable.

The circuit has quite a high level of gain, and a well decoupled supply is essential. This decoupling is provided by C1, R4, C6, and C7.

Send/Receive Switching

The send/receive switching is very straightforward: this two-way system having one master unit and one slave, in the conventional manner. S1 is the send/receive switch which is, of course, situated in the master unit. In the receive position the master speaker is connected to the output of the amplifier by S1b, and the slave speaker (which then acts as the microphone) is connected to the amplifier input via S1a. In the send position these two connections are reversed.

S1 should preferably be a biased switch (suitable push button types are available at the time of writing) which is biased to the receive mode. Then it is merely necessary for S3 in the slave unit to be closed, and the operator to speak into the microphone, in order for the slave unit to call the master one. The function of S3 is simply to connect the battery situated in the slave unit to the amplifier, and thus switch the unit on.

The reason for using a biased switch in the S1 position is that after each session when the unit has been used, this switch will automatically return to the receive position, enabling the slave unit to call the master one. If an ordinary switch is used in the S1 position then it will be necessary for the operator of the master unit to always remember to return S1 to the receive position at the end of each session, as if it is left in the send position it will obviously be impossible for the slave unit to call the master one.

For the master unit to call the slave one it is merely necessary for S2 to be closed, S1 to be switched to the send position, and then for the operator to talk into the microphone.

Construction

The component layout of the unit is not particularly critical as although the circuit has quite a high gain and the input and output are in phase, there is little likelihood of instability due to stray feedback as the input impedance of the amplifier is so low. However, care must be taken with the earthing arrangement used as it is easy to produce feedback loops here. For example, the earthy input lead from the slave unit should not be connected to the speaker at the master unit, and then to the amplifier via the speaker lead. It must be connected direct to the amplifier component panel.

A three core cable is used to connect the two stations, and thin mains lead is probably the best type of cable to use here. The prototype intercom has been tested using a cable about 12 Metres long, but it would probably be possible to use a much longer cable if required.

Note that although this circuit is put forward here as an intercom, it could easily be adapted for use as either a baby alarm or a doorphone.

Two way Intercom Components

Resistors. All miniature ¼ watt 5 or 10%.
R1   5.6k.
R2   8.2 ohms.
R3   1.2 Meg.
R4   1k.
R5   8.2 ohms.

Capacitors.
C1   220mfd. 10v.w.
C2   100mfd. 6v.w.
C3   100nf plastic foil or ceramic
C4   470nf plastic foil.
C5   100nf plastic foil.
C6   10mfd. 10v.w.
C7   220mfd. 10v.w.
C8   100mfd. 10v.w.

Semiconductors
IC1   LM380N.
Tr1   BC109C.

Switches
S1   DPDT biased push button switch.
S2   SPST toggle or push button switch.
S3   SPST toggle or push button switch.

Miscellaneous.
Two miniature (about 66mm diameter) 8 ohm loudspeakers.
Two 9 volt batteries, connecting cable, cases, component panel
etc.

Telephone Repeater

It can sometimes happen that the ringing of a telephone can be
missed, such as when one is working in an out building, or
perhaps when listening to music or a T.V. set in a room which
is some distance away from the phone. This problem can be
overcome by using a telephone monitor, a device which relays
the telephone bells sound to the user.

It is illegal to make an unauthorised direct connection to a Post Office telephone, and so a device of this type must be designed to be activated by the sound of the bell so that no direct connection is required. The circuit diagram of the telephone monitor is shown in Fig. 24, and as can be seen from this, the circuit is very simple with only two active devices being employed.

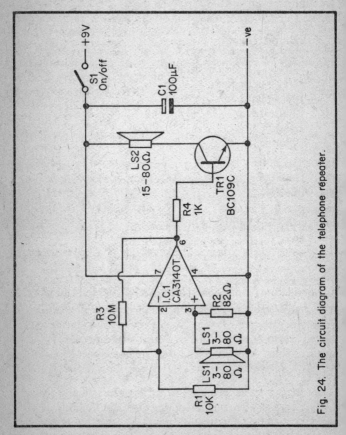

Fig. 24. The circuit diagram of the telephone repeater.

The unit could be designed to pick up the sound from the bell, amplify it, and send it to a speaker situated near the user. The main problem with this arrangement is that the circuit would probably need to have a fairly high standby current, and if the circuit is to be battery operated this would make it rather expensive to run. This circuit uses the basic arrangement described above, but it does provide linear amplification of the sound from the bell. In fact it half-wave rectifies it, and produces a considerable amount of distortion. This does not matter, of course, as the unit is not called upon to handle speech or music, but is only required to produce some form of audio output in order to attract the attention of the user. As the circuit only handles one polarity of half cycles and can produce considerable distortion it is an easy matter to produce a design that has a low standby current.

A low impedance speaker is used as the microphone, and the output of this is direct coupled to the non-inverting input of IC1, which is used as a high gain non-inverting amplifier. This circuit is ground referenced and uses a single supply rail. It therefore only handles positive output half cycles from the microphone. R3 and R1 set the voltage gain of IC1 at approximately 60dB. (1,000 times).

The base of Tr1 is driven from the output of IC1 via current limiting resistor R4. LS2 forms the collector load for Tr1. Under quiescent conditions the output of the IC will be at virtually the same potential as the negative supply rail. and Tr1 will therefore be cut off. Positive output half-cycles from the microphone will cause the output of IC1 to swing heavily positive, with Tr1 being biased hard on in consequence. Thus, the noise from the telephone bell causes a series of pulses to be fed to the loudspeaker, generating a buzzing sound.

S1 is the on/off switch and C1 provides supply decoupling. The quiescent current of the circuit is only about 1mA. or so, and so the battery (which can consist of six HP7 size cells in a plastic holder) will have an extremely long life.

Construction

Although the circuit has a very high level of gain, and the input and output are in phase, there is little risk of instability due to stray feedback. This is partly due to the low input impedance of the circuit, and partly due to the fact that under quiescent conditions the output stage is cut off. The component layout is therefore uncritical.

Obviously either the microphone or the speaker must be remotely located from the rest of the circuit. As both the input and output are at a fairly low impedance it is acceptable to have a long lead at either. However, it is probably best to have the unit situated near the telephone, and have a long lead connecting to a remotely located speaker. Having a long lead at the input could possibly result in stray pick up of mains hum etc., which could in turn lead to spurious operation of the unit.

It is worth noting that although this circuit is put forward here as a telephone monitor, it can also be used as a doorbell or doorknocker monitor.

Telephone Repeater Components

Resistors. All are miniature ¼ watt 5 or 10%.
R1   10k.
R2   82 ohms.
R3   10 Meg.
R4   1k.

Capacitors.
C1   100mfd. 10v.w.

Semiconductors.
Tr1   BC109C
IC1   CA314OT

Switch.
S1   SPST toggle type

Miscellaneous
15 to 80 ohm loudspeaker, and 8 to 80 ohm speaker (used as mic).
6 volt battery, battery connector, case component panel, etc.

Metal Detector

Until a few years ago there were very few metal locator designs published, but they have proliferated in recent years and now rank extremely high in terms of popularity. Simple BFO designs are particularly popular as they offer quite a high level of performance but are nonetheless relatively inexpensive an easy to construct.

The circuit diagram of a simple BFO type metal locator is shown in Fig. 25. Detectors of this type operate on the principle that if two radio transmitters are on virtually the same frequency, a nearby receiver adjusted to pick up their signals will produce what is termed a 'beat note'. The frequency of this note is equal to the difference in the frequencies of the two transmitters. Thus if one transmitter operates at 124kHz, and the other transmits at 125kHz, the difference between the two frequencies is 1kHz, and a 1kHz audio note will be produced from the receiver. This beat note is actually a form of heterodyning, which was described earlier in this book. This effect can be demonstrated by tuning over the MW band on an ordinary broadcast receiver after dark. Wherever there are two stations on similar frequencies a beat note will be produced, and the beat frequencies will range from less than 1Hz (on stations that are supposed to be on the same channel) to a few kHz (produced by stations on adjacent channels).

In a BFO metal locator the two transmitters are simply oscillators, of course, and they do not radiate the signal, but are capacitively coupled into a very basic type of radio receiver. In a conventional arrangement both oscillators are of L/C type. One operates at a fixed frequency, and the search

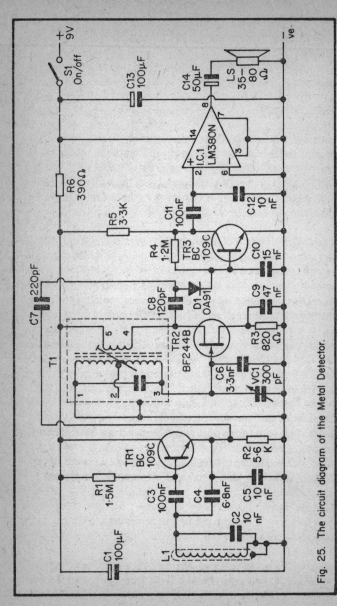

Fig. 25. The circuit diagram of the Metal Detector.

94

coil forms the inductive part of the tuned circuit. The other oscillator has an ordinary L/C tuned circuit, and is made tuneable.

In practice the tuneable oscillator is tuned just below the frequency of the fixed oscillator so as to produce an audio output frequency of perhaps only a few Hz. Metal objects which are brought close to the search coil act rather like the core in an ordinary variable inductor, and the closer they are brought to the coil, the higher they make its inductance (this is the effect of most metals anyway). Of course, a small metal object even when brought fairly close to the search coil will not have much of an effect on its inductance, and this is why it is necessary to employ the BFO principle.

The change in inductance might only be sufficient to alter the operating frequency of the search coil oscillator by a few Hz, which is very little when one considers that the oscillator will probably have a nominal operating frequency of 100kHz or more. However, the user of the equipment is not monitoring the frequency of the search coil oscillator directly (it's at far too high a frequency to be heard anyway), but is monitoring the difference in the frequency between this oscillator and the tunable reference oscillator. As explained earlier, this need only be a few Hz, and so a reduction in this by a few Hz can hardly be missed!

If we now consider the practical circuit of Fig. 25; L1 is the search coil, and this is used in a common collector Colpitts oscillator which has Tr1 as its active element. The tuneable oscillator Tr2 in a straight forward f.e.t. inductive feedback oscillator. This oscillator is broadly tuned by the core of T1, and VC1 provides fine tuning. T1 is an ordinary 470kHz IF transformer, but its internal tuning capacitance is shunted by C6 and VC1, which reduce the operating frequency to the required amount.

It should perhaps be explained here that for a metal locator to be legally operated in the U.K. it must operate in the band from 0 to 150kHz, and preferably between 85 and 90kHz, or

110 and 145 kHz. A Pipe Finder/Metal locator licence is required, and at the time of writing this costs £1.20 for five years. Licence application forms can be obtained from The Home Office, Radio Regulatory Department, Waterloo Bridge House, Waterloo Road, London, SE1. A certain amount of technical information must be provided with the application, and the necessary information is provided here.

The nominal operating frequency of the unit is 125kHz, and this has been checked by the author using a digital frequency meter.

Returning to Fig. 25; the outputs from the two oscillators are coupled to diode detector D1 via C7 and C8. C10 provides RF filtering at the output of the detector, and the remaining audio signal is fed direct to Tr3 base. Tr3 is used as a high gain common emitter amplifier. The output from this stage is fed to the IC audio output stage. This uses an LM380N IC in the non-inverting mode. C12 provides additional RF filtering and helps to prevent the circuit from becoming unstable.

C14 provides DC blocking at the output, and the circuit can be used to feed speakers having an impedance in the range 35 to 80 ohms. Headphones having an impedance of 8 ohms or more can also be used, and even a crystal earpiece is suitable. There is some advantage in using headphones as they cut out extraneous noise to some degree, and provide better volume. This makes it easier to concentrate on the audio tone. Headphones (or an earpiece) also have the advantage of avoiding any possible annoyance to other people.

C1, R6, and C13 are the supply decoupling components, and S1 is the on/off switch. Power can be obtained from a medium capacity 9 volt battery such as a PP6 or a PP7, and the quiescent current consumption is about 15mA or so.

Construction

As far as component layout is concerned, the circuit is not unduly critical. Mechanical construction is not too critical either, and the unit can either be built as a small hand held unit for locating pipes or cables in walls (along the lines shown in Fig. 26a) or it can be built along the lines of a mine detector (as shown in Fig. 26b). In either case it is absolutely essential that the construction of the unit is carried out to reasonably high standards so that the entire assembly is fairly rigid. Otherwise it is likely that changes in the search coil oscillator frequency will be caused by wires flapping around, or similar physical problems. This would obviously render the unit difficult or even impossible to use effectively.

It is extremely important that the circuit is not modified in any way which could alter the operating frequency of the unit. In particular, the values of C2, C4, C5 and C6 should not be altered, and these components should be good quality types such as polystyrene or mica capacitors, and should have tolerances of 5% or better. T1 is a Denco IFT13/470kHz type I.F. transformer, and an alternative should not be substituted for this. The search coil should be wound exactly as described below, and its size and number of turns should not be altered. Failing to observe these points could result in the operating frequency of the unit being significantly altered, and possibly could result in this frequency being taken outside the legal band limits.

L1 is wound on a temporary former which has a diameter of 150mm. The author used a 2.5 litre paint can, but if nothing suitable can be found around the house a cardboard tube of the required diameter can be made. L1 consists of precisely 20 turns of ordinary PVC covered multistrand hook-up wire. The author employed 7/02mm wire, but the exact type does not seem to be too important. When 20 turns have been completed, remove the coil from the former and use a few bands of insulation tape to prevent the coil from falling apart. It is then advisable to wrap the coil in aluminium foil (cooking foil is suitable), leaving a gap in this sheathing at the point where

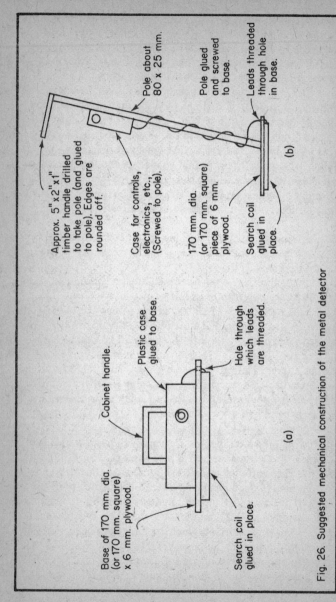

Fig. 26. Suggested mechanical construction of the metal detector

Base of 170 mm. dia. (or 170 mm. square) x 6 mm. plywood.

Cabinet handle.

Plastic case glued to base.

Hole through which leads are threaded.

Search coil glued in place.

(a)

Approx. 5" x 2" x 1" timber handle drilled (and glued to pole). Edges are rounded off.

Pole about 80 x 25 mm.

Case for controls, electronics, etc., (Screwed to pole).

170 mm. dia. (or 170 mm. square) piece of 6 mm. plywood.

Search coil glued in place.

Pole glued and screwed to base.

Leads threaded through hole in base.

(b)

leadout wires emerge from the coil, so that there is not quite a complete coil of foil. This gap is important as the sheath would otherwise form a shorted turn which could adversely affect the unit. Make sure that the coil is completely covered apart from this gap.

The aluminium foil forms what is normally called a Faraday Shield, and it is needed to prevent ground capacity effects. This is where placing the search coil near the ground causes a slight change in the frequency of the search coil oscillator. This effect obviously makes the unit slightly difficult to use unless steps are taken to eliminate it. However, although the use of a Faraday Shield is recommended, it is not absolutely essential.

Connect the shield to whichever leadout wire of the coil will connect to the negative supply rail of the detector circuit. It is a little difficult to make the connection to the shield as it is not possible to solder directly to aluminium unless a special type of solder is used. The method used by the author was to wind several turns of about 22swg tinned copper wire tightly around the shield at some convenient point, and then heavily tin this wire with solder. The connection can then be made to the wire without any difficulty.

It is then a good idea to cover the coil with a layer or two of PVC insulation tape which is tightly wound around the coil. This will give the coil rigidity, make it look neater, and will provide a degree of weather proofing. The coil is then ready to be glued in position using a generous amount of epoxy adhesive.

Adjustment and Use

Initially VC1 should be set for about half maximum capacitance. When the unit is first switched on there may be an audio tone from the speaker, and if so, the core of T1 is adjusted using a proper trimming tool to zero beat this tone (i.e. the core of T1 is adjusted to produce a tone which is so low in pitch that it cannot be heard). If no audio tone is produced, the core of T1 should be adjusted in an attempt to produce a tone, and once this signal has been located it is zero beated.

In use, VC1 is adjusted to produce an audio output of a very low pitch. This can be achieved by offsetting VC1 slightly either side of the zero beat setting. It will be found that with VC1 adjusted in one direction there is a drop in pitch from the output signal when the search coil is placed near a metalic object. If it is offset in the other direction there will be a rise in the pitch of the output signal when the search coil is placed near something metallic. Obviously the unit can be used with VC1 offset in either direction, but most people find a drop in pitch more readily detectable than a similar rise in pitch.

Whether results obtained are good, bad, or indifferent depends to a large extent upon the skill of the operator, and a certain amount of practice is required before the user will obtain optimum results. With the prototype it was possible to detect small objects such as ½p coins and even a .177 airgun pellet, provided these objects were on or very close to the surface. Larger coins such as 2p and 10p pieces could be located at depths of up to a couple of inches or so. Large metal objects can be detected at depths of up to about one foot.

Most finds produce only a very small change in the frequency of the output tone, and for this reason it is essential to adjust VC1 for a very low pitch output. A change in frequency of 10Hz will obviously be much more apparent on a 20Hz signal than it will on a 2,000 Hz one.

Metal Detector Components

Resistors. All are miniature ¼ watt 5 or 10%.
R1   1.5 Meg.
R2   5.6k.

R3 820 ohms.
R4 1.2 Meg.
R5 3.3k.
R6 390 ohms.

Capacitors.
C1   100mfd. 10v.w.
C2   10nf polystyrene or mica 5% or better.
C3   100nf plastic foil.
C4   6.8nf polystyrene or mica 5% or better.
C5   10nf polystyrene or mica 5% or batter.
C6   3.3nf polystyrene or mica 5% or better.
C7   220pf ceramic plate, etc.
C8   120pf ceramic plate, etc.
C9   47nf plastic foil.
C10 15nf plastic foil.
C11 100nf plastic foil.
C12 10nf plastic foil.
C13 100mfd. 10v.w.
C14 50mfd. 10v.w.
VC1 300pf solid dielectric (Jackson)

Semiconductors.
Tr1 BC109C
Tr2 BF244B.
Tr3 BC109C.
IC1 LM380N.
D1   OA91.

Switch.
S1   SPST toggle type.

Miscellaneous.
Wire etc. for L1 (see text).
Denco IFT 13/470kHz (T1).
35 to 80 ohm impedance loudspeaker or headphones.
9 volt battery, case connecting wire, materials for frame, etc.

Rain Alarm

Units of this type are amongst the most simple of electronic projects, but they are also very useful. The circuit diagram of a rain alarm is shown in Fig. 27.

In common with other designs of this type, the circuit relies on the fact that water has a fairly low resistance, provided it contains a certain amount of salts or other dissolved impurities. Pure water is actually an insulator, but rain and tap water are far from pure (in this context of the word 'pure'), and so a rain sensor can simply consist of two parallel strips of metal separated by an insulating material. In the absence of rain there will be virtually an infinite impedance between the two metal strips, but this will fall to an impedance of perhaps only a few k ohms if a raindrop bridges the strips.

In the circuit of Fig. 27, Tr1 is used as a switch which is operated by the sensor. Tr1 is used in the emitter follower mode. In the absence of rain on the sensor Tr1 will receive no base current, and it will be cut off. When the sensor is activated Tr1 will receive a strong base current, and it will be switched hard on. Virtually the full supply rail potential will then be supplied to the alarm circuit from Tr1 emitter. The circuit is very economic to operate as no significant supply current flows until rain is sensed.

The alarm circuit is based on a LM380N IC which is used as a Wien Bridge oscillator. C1, R1, C2, and R3 form the Wien network which provide the necessary frequency selective positive feedback. The circuit oscillates at a frequency of approximately 14kHz. The voltage gain of the LM380N is set by an internal feedback network at a level of 50 times, which is far higher than is required for a Wien Bridge oscillator. A voltage gain of only a little over three times is required in this application. R2 and R4 are used in a discrete feedback network which reduce the closed loop gain of the circuit to about 4.7 times. This is a little higher than is absolutely necessary, but this is an advantage as it results in a more strident and piercing tone being produced by the unit.

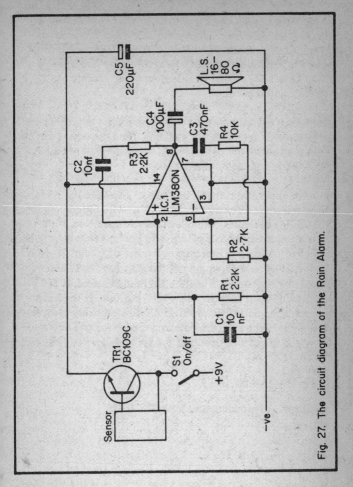

Fig. 27. The circuit diagram of the Rain Alarm.

Construction

The component layout is not particularly critical, and should present no problems. A suitable sensor can be etched from a piece of copper laminate board using p.c.b. techniques, and there are other possibilities. For instance, a piece of strip-board can be used. Alternate copper strips are connected together using link wires, and then this network is connected to Tr1 base. The remaining copper strips are then similarly wired up and connected to Tr1 collector. Whatever type of sensor is employed, it is advisable to employ one having a fairly large area, so that it will be activated quickly at the onset of any rain fall.

Units such as this can be employed in other applications, such as water level detectors, for example. Here the sensor can be arranged so that the alarm sounds when the water in a bath reaches some predetermined level.

In most applications it will be necessary to have the sensor mounted some distance away from the main unit, and a long connecting cable here will not upset the operation of the unit. S1 is an ordinary on/off switch, and the unit should only be switched on when it is necessary to check for rainfall. This avoids unnecessary sounding of the alarm and consequent wasted battery drain. When the alarm does sound, it can be silenced by switching S1 to the 'off' position. If the alarm sounds when S1 is first switched on, this probably just means that some rain has accumulated on the sensor and needs to be wiped off, rather than that the unit has developed a fault.

Rain Alarm Components

Resistors. All are miniature ¼ watt 5 or 10%.
R1   2.2k.
R2   2.7k.
R3   2.2k.
R4   10k.

Capacitors.
C1   10nf plastic foil.
C2   10nf plastic foil.
C3   470nf plastic foil.
C4   100mfd. 10v.w.
C5   220mfd. 10v.w.

Semiconductors.
IC1   LM380N
Tr1   BC109C.

Switch
S1   SPST toggle type.

Miscellaneous.
Materials for sensor.
15 to 80 ohm loudspeaker.
Case, connecting cable, 9 volt battery, etc.

Power Controller

A power controller of the type used for lamp dimming, drill speed controlling, etc., is another example of a very simple but extremely useful electronic project. The controller described here can handle loads of up to about 200 Watts or so, or up to about 500 Watts if the triac is fitted with suitable heatsinking. The circuit diagram of the controller is shown in Fig. 28, and this is a standard diac-triac type circuit.

Circuits of this type control the power fed to the load by means of a switching action. If full power is applied to the load the circuit must be almost continuously switched to the 'on' mode. In order to reduce the power in the load to half its normal level, for instance, the circuit must be switched to the 'on' state for only half of each input half-cycle.

This might at first sight appear to be an overcomplicated way of controlling the output power, but it has the advantage of wasting very little power in the control element, since it is either switched on or off, and theoretically it consumes no power in either state. In practice the control element provides some series resistance, and therefore does have to dissipate some power, but it is nothing like as inefficient as using some form of series resistor to control the load.

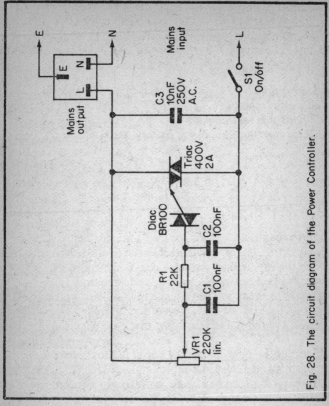

Fig. 28. The circuit diagram of the Power Controller.

The control element in this circuit is the triac. This is normally in the 'off' state, but it can be switched on by the application of a small gate current. Once triggered, the triac will remain switched on until the current flowing through it reaches virtually zero, even if the gate current is removed. The gate of the triac is connected to the neutral mains lead via the load, VR1, R1, and the diac.

With VR1 adjusted for minimum resistance the trigger voltage of the diac will be reached very early in each mains half-cycle. When the diac fires, its impedance falls to a very low level and C2 is discharged into the gate of the triac. This switches the

106

triac on until the end of the half cycle. This results in virtually full power being applied to the load, although there is obviously some loss of power as the triac does not switch on at the very beginning of each half-cycle. However, this does not significantly reduce the output from the controller.

If VR1 is adjusted for increased resistance it will take slightly longer for the trigger voltage of the diac to be developed across C2. This is because VR1, C1, R1, and C2 form a C-R delay network, and the higher the resistance of VR1, the longer the delay produced by this network.

Obviously this delay results in the first part of each mains half-cycle being cut out, and a consequent reduction in the power fed to the load. In fact, if VR1 is adjusted for maximum resistance the delay will be sufficiently long to prevent the diac and triac from being triggered at all. The circuit thus enables the power applied to the load to be varied from virtually full power to zero.

One problem with circuits of this type is that the diac and triac operate at very high speeds, and as they switch on they therefore generate RF signals. These signals are usually strong enough to interfere with any AM radios in the vicinity of the controller, unless some measure(s) to attenuate them are taken. In this circuit C3 is used to provide a degree of suppression, although this will not be totally effective.

It should, however, reduce radio interference to an insignificant level.

Construction

It is advisable to house this project in a plastic case. If a metal case, or a partly metal case is employed, then the metal parts must be properly earthed. The circuit can easily be constructed on a p.c.b., tag strip, or using any other preferred method of construction. The component assembly should be mounted using nylon bolts, or if metal ones are used, they must be earthed. VR1 should be a type having a plastic spindle, and it should be fitted with a plastic control knob. The output socket can be an ordinary surface mounting mains outlet socket, so that the controlled equipment can be plugged direct into the controller. C1 and C2 should have working voltages of 250 volts DC or more, and C3 should be capable of handling 250 volts AC (a component having a DC working voltage of 500 volts or more should be suitable). Remember that the circuit connects direct to the mains supply, and do not touch or work on any of the wiring while the unit is plugged into the mains.

Power Controller Components

Resistors.
R1   22k ¼ watt 5 or 10%.
VR1 220k lin. carbon.

Capacitors.
C1   100nf plastic foil 100V. or more.
C2   100nf plastic foil 100V. or more.
C3   10nf plastic foil or mixed dielectric 250V AC or more.

Semiconductors.
Diac BR100.
Triac 400V. 2 Amp. TO5 or TO39 case.

Switch.
S1   SPST toggle type.

Miscellaneous.
Case, surface mounting mains outlet, mains cable, control knob, etc.

Flash Slave Unit

Flash units are very inexpensive, and are very popular. It is therefore only to be expected that photoflash slave units will be extremely popular as electronic constructional projects.

For those who are unfamiliar with these units, they provide a means of triggering a secondary flashgun without the need for any direct connection to either the camera or the main flash unit. The photoflash slave unit works by triggering the secondary gun when it picks up the flash of light from the main unit.

The main advantage of using two flash units is that photographs taken with a single gun often have rather sharp and unnatural shadows. This can be overcome by using two or more flashguns, so that fill-in illumination can be provided.

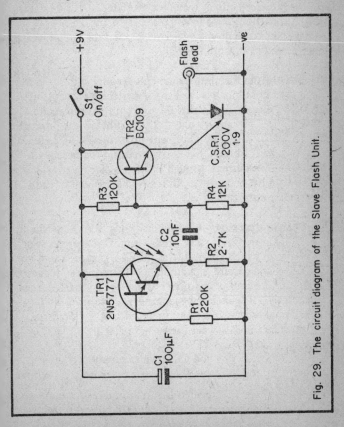

Fig. 29. The circuit diagram of the Slave Flash Unit.

Fig. 29. Shows the circuit diagram of a simple photoflash slave unit. The flash detector circuit utilises Tr1, which is a Photo-Darlington transistor which is used here in the emitter follower mode. R2 is the emitter load for Tr1, and when a light flash is received by Tr1 the collector—emitter impedance of this photocell is reduced, and a positive voltage spike is developed across R2. R1 is used to reverse bias the base of Tr1, and thus slightly reduce the sensitivity of the photocell circuit. This may at first sight seem to be counter productive, since this will obviously reduce the sensitivity of the unit. However, unless this is done there is a strong possibility that the photocell circuit would be saturated in fairly bright lighting conditions. This would make it impossible for the voltage spike to be produced across R2, and the circuit would be prevented from working at all.

The output from the photocell circuit is coupled to the gate of the thyristor (which is used as the switching element) by way of DC blocking capacitor C2, and emitter follower transistor Tr2. R3 and R4 bias Tr2 to just below the point at which CSR1 is triggered. Thus, when the voltage spike via C2 is received at Tr1 base CSR1 is triggered and the flashgun is fired. When the current through CSR1 has died away after the flashgun has been triggered, it switches off and is ready for the next operation.

At first sight the emitter follower stage may seem superfluous, since it does not provide any voltage gain. However, most of the thyristors which are readily available at present are rather insensitive, and require gate currents of 20mA. or so for reliable operation. The emitter follower buffer stage is therefore used to match the fairly high impedance of the photocell circuit to the comparatively low input impedance of the thyristor. This provides improved sensitivity and reliability.

S1 is the on/off switch and C1 provides supply decoupling. Current consumption from the 9 volt battery is very low, and is typically only about 1mA.

Construction

The layout of this very simple circuit is not critical, and should not present any problems, even for a beginner. The unit can be built in a clear plastic box, so that Tr1 is not isolated from the light produced by the main flashgun. Alternatively, an opaque case can be used, and Tr1 can be mounted on the exterior of this. Note that the curved surface of the case of Tr1 is the light sensitive side, and that for most reliable results this should be aimed at the main flash unit. Of course, when the slave unit is used in close proximity to the main flashgun, there is no need to bother about aiming Tr1. This is only necessary when using the unit at about the limit of its range, which should be at least 30 feet (indoors) when using a low powered main flashgun. The maximum range will be less out of doors as there will not be walls, ceilings, and other objects to help reflect the light from the main flashgun onto Tr1.

It is essential that the flash lead is connected to the correct polarity as the thyristor cannot operate properly unless this is correct. Connecting the flashlead the wrong way round will not damage the circuit, and so trial and error can be used here if no better method is possible.

Flash Slave Unit Components

Resistors. All are miniature ¼ watt 5 or 10%.
R1   220k.
R2   2.7k.
R3   120k.
R4   12k.

Capacitors.
C1   100mfd. 10v.w.
C2   10nf plastic foil.

Semiconductors.
Tr1   2N4777.
Tr2   BC109.
CSR1 200 PIV 1 Amp. T05 or T039 case.

Switch.
S1   SPST toggle type.

Miscellaneous.
Case, 9 volt battery, connecting wire, flash extension
lead, etc.

CHAPTER 4

TEST EQUIPMENT

In general the field of test equipment is not one of the most popular areas of amateur electronics. However, there are some projects in this field which are useful and they will be covered in this final Chapter.

High Impedance Voltmeter

It is perhaps not generally realized that readings obtained using an ordinary multimeter can be misleading, particularly when it comes to DC voltage readings. The main problem is that the power to operate the meter must be drawn from the circuit under test when an ordinary passive multimeter circuit is used. Most multimeters use a 50 micro-amp. meter movement as although it is possible to produce meters of higher sensitivity, inevitably such meters are less robust and therefore not particularly suitable for general service work. There are actually a few multimeters which are reasonably robust and have meter movements of a higher sensitivity than 50 micro-amps., but even these have only moderately high sensitivities and draw an appreciable current from the test circuit.

Usually the fact that a few tens of micro-amps are drawn from the circuit being tested is of no consequence, but when testing fairly high impedance circuits this is not the case. If there are only two or three micro-amps. flowing in part of a circuit, it is obviously impossible to accurately measure voltages present there using a meter which would need to draw off some twenty or thirty micro-amps. in order to give a realistic reading. Connecting such a meter to a high impedance circuit of this type will simply result in the circuit voltages falling to very low levels with these low readings then being obtained on the meter.

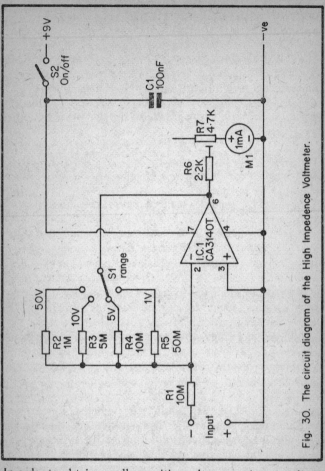

Fig. 30. The circuit diagram of the High Impedence Voltmeter.

In order to obtain a really sensitive voltmeter using an ordinary moving coil meter it is necessary to use an amplifier ahead of the meter. This is basically all a high impedance voltmeter consists of. In common with most units of this type, the circuit described here has an input impedance of about 10 Meg. ohms on all ranges. Four ranges are covered and these are 1V., 5V., 10V., and 50V. FSD. These correspond to sensitivities of 10M/V; 2.0M/V; 1.0M/V and 200k/V. respectively. This is,

114

of course, much better than the 20k/V. of a standard multimeter.

The circuit diagram of the high impedance voltmeter is shown in Fig. 30. IC1 is an operational amplifier which is used in the inverting mode. R6, R7, and M1 form a conventional voltmeter circuit which is connected at the output of the IC, R7 is adjusted to produce a voltmeter sensitivity of 5 volts FSD here.

The gain of IC1 is determined by the feedback resistor network which consists of R1 and whichever of the resistors in the series R2 to R5 is switched into circuit by S1. The latter is the range switch. The closed loop voltage gain of IC1 is equal to the resistance between its output and inverting input divided by R1. Thus, with S1 in the 1V. position the voltage gain of IC1 is 50M divided by 10M, or 5 in other words. This raises the basic 5 volt FSD sensitivity of the circuit to the required 1 volt FSD. In the 5V. position of S1 the voltage gain of IC1 is obviously unity, and so an overall sensitivity of 5 volts FSD. is obtained.

In the 10V. and 50V. positions of S1 the circuit actually acts as an attenuator as far as voltage is concerned. However, the input impedance of the entire circuit is much higher than the input impedance of the voltmeter connected at the output of the amplifier. The circuit therefore always provides current amplification regardless of what position S1 is switched to, and it therefore always boosts the input impedance of the circuit by a considerable amount, even though the voltage gain of the circuit may be less than unity.

What is termed a 'virtual earth' is produced at the inverting input of IC1, and so the input impedance of the circuit is equal to the value of R1, which is 10 Meg. in this case. By virtual earth it is merely meant that the feedback action maintains the inverting input at the same potential as the non-inverting input (which is connected to earth). For example, if with S1 in the 5 volt position an input potential of 3 volts is connected to the circuit, the inverting input will be taken negative of the non-inverting input. The output potential of IC1 is equal to its voltage gain (about 200,000) multiplied by the voltage difference across its inputs. Obviously only a very small difference is required here in order to send the output fully positive or negative. However, in this case the output will only swing three volts positive due to the presence of R4. By a simple potential divider action there will then be 0 volts at the inverting input, and the circuit will be balanced. It should be apparent from this how the feedback resistors set the closed loop voltage gain of the circuit.

Although this basic configuration is a quite conventional one, the circuit is a little unusual in that it does not have dual balanced power supplies, as are normally employed with circuits of this type. The CA314OT is a modern operational amplifier IC with its inputs at or close to the negative supply rail potential. It also has an output which is capable of swinging down to virtually the negative supply rail voltage. This enables it to function perfectly satisfactorily with only a single supply rail. Note though, that the 741C IC cannot be substitute for the CA3140T in this application.

Construction And Adjustment

Since this circuit is only intended to operate at DC the component layout is not critical. However, it must be borne in mind that the circuit has a high impedance, and will work at low frequencies. It could, therefore, pick up mains hum and other forms of electrical interference. These could prevent the meter from zeroing properly even with no input signal applied. To avoid this it is recommended that the unit should be housed in a metal cabinet, and that the cabinet should be earthed to the negative supply rail.

When the completed unit is first switched on it is possible that there may be some slight positive deflection of the meter, even if the circuit is adequately screened. This is simply due to the fact that the output of the IC will not swing right

116

down to the negative supply rail potential, although this offset voltage will be extremely low, and a deflection of the meter will be extremely small. It may well be unnoticeable, and at worst it will be so small as to be easily corrected by mechanically zeroing the meter.

Probably the easiest way of calibrating the unit is to obtain a 9 volt battery and then accurately measure its voltage using a multimeter. Switch the high impedance voltmeter circuit to the 10 volt range, connect the battery to the input, and then adjust R7 to produce the appropriate voltage reading. The unit is then ready for use.

Components

R1 to R5 should all be close tolerance (2% or better) components, but apart from R2, suitable components do not seem to be readily available to the amateur. The easiest way around this problem is to make these resistors from several 5% components wired in series. This is necessary in the case of R3 and R5 anyway as components of these values are not available. This does not guarantee an accuracy of more than 5% on these values, but in practice a higher accuracy is almost certain to be obtained.

High Impedance Voltmeter Components

Resistors.
R1   10 Meg. close tolerance (e.g. four 2.2 Meg. and one 1.2 Meg. 5% resistors wired in series).
R2   1 Meg. 2% or better.
R3   5 Meg. close tolerance (e.g. five 1 Meg. 5% resistors wired in series).
R4   10 Meg. close tolerance (e.g. as for R1).
R5   50M close tolerance (e.g. five 10 Meg. 5% resistored wired in series).
R6   2.2k ¼ watt 5 or 10%.
R7   4.7k preset.

Capacitor
C1   100nf plastic foil.

Semiconductor.
IC1   CA3140T

Switches.
S1   SPST toggle type.
S2   4 way 3 pole rotary (only one pole used).

Meter.
M1   1mA. moving coil type.

Miscellaneous.
Case, 9 volt battery, test prods, input sockets, component panel control knob, connecting wire, etc.

Transistor Tester

Transistors feature in virtually all contemporary electronic designs, and they cannot be satisfactorily tested using most multimeters. Thus some form of simple transistor tester is virtually an essential piece of test gear for the amateur electronics workshop. Of course, transistors have many parameters, but the two most important ones are gain and leakage, and it is these which most transistor testers are designed to measure. The circuit which appears in Fig. 31 is no exception to this.

Leakage is extremely easy to measure, and this is simply the current which flows between the emitter and collector terminals if they are fed from a voltage source. The base is left unconnected. In order to measure leakage using this circuit it is merely necessary to set the supply and meter polarity to suit the type of transistor which is to be tested (pnp or npn) using S1, and then connect the collector and emitter terminals of the device under test to the appropriate test terminals. Meter M1 will then register the leakage current. Resistor R4 is connected in series with the meter to protect it against any serious overloading.

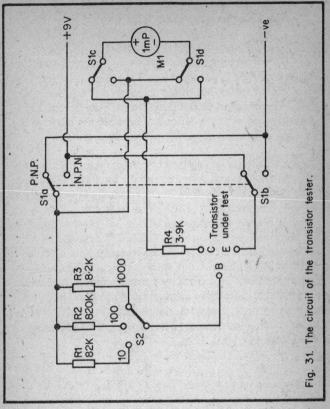

Fig. 31. The circuit of the transistor tester.

Silicon transistors have very low leakage currents, the actual figure usually being only a small fraction of a micro-amp. Good silicon devices should therefore cause no deflection of M1. Germanium transistors have comparatively large leakage currents, and may therefore cause a small deflection of the meter. Output and power types can cause a considerable deflection of the meter, and still be quite serviceable devices.

In order to measure the gain of the test device it is necessary to also connect the base terminal to the appropriate test terminal. A base current will then be supplied to the test device via R1, R2 or R3, depending upon which of these is switched into circuit by S2. These resistors provide base currents of 100, 10, and 1 micro-amp. respectively. Gain is equal to collector current divided by base current, and so these base currents FSD gain values on M1 of 10, 100, and 1,000 respectively. If the device under test has a negligible leakage current it is possible to read the gain of the test device direct off the meter, but this is obviously not possible if a fairly heavy leakage current flows through the device. The gain is then equal to the difference between the readings obtained with and without the base lead connected.

The circuit cannot be adjusted to measure gain at particular collector voltages and currents, and the same is true for leakage tests. Therefore the readings obtained should only be used as a guide to the usefulness, or otherwise, of a device. Results will probably be very reliable when testing small signal transistors, and it is when checking power types that false readings may be obtained. This is because power transistors are intended to operate at high currents, and their gain figures are usually quoted at quite a high collector current (perhaps as much as several amps). This tester measures gain at up to 1mA., the exact figure depending upon the reading obtained. This can result in rather low readings being produced when testing power devices.

Construction

The circuit is so simple that there should be no problems with regard to construction. As so few components are used, point to point wiring is probably the most convenient form of construction to use for this project. The connections to the device, under test can be made by way of short test leads terminated in miniature crocodile clips. The unit does not require an on/off switch as no significant current flows from the battery until a test transistor is connected into circuit.

Transistor Tester Components

Resistors. All miniature ¼ watt 5%.
R1   82k.
R2   820k.
R3   8.2 Meg.
R4   3.9k.

Switches.
S1   2 way 4 pole (use 3 way 4 pole with adjustable end
      stop set for 2 way operation).
S2   3 way 4 pole (only one pole used).

Meter.
M1   1mA. moving coil type.

Miscellaneous.
9 volt battery, case, crocodile clips, control knobs, wire, etc.

Continuity Tester

This is one of the most simple pieces of test equipment and
merely consists of a circuit which will show whether or not
there is electrical continuity between two points. A multimeter
switched to an ohms range can be used for this type of testing,
but such an arrangement is often rather inconvenient as it
provides only a visual indication. This makes it necessary to
look away from the equipment being tested in order to ascertain
whether or not there is continuity. This can be avoided by
using a circuit which provides an audio signal to indicate
continuity, and it is a tester of this type which is described
here. Its circuit diagram appears in Fig. 32.

Tr1 is used in a phase shift oscillator circuit which operates
at a frequency of about 1kHz. Tr1 is used in the common
emitter configuration with R4 acting as the collector load
and R3 providing base biasing. There are three 60 degree phase
shift networks which are comprised of C4 − R1, C2 − R2,

and C3 — the input impedance of Tr1. Thus, although the input and output of Tr1 are 180 degrees out of phase, the phase shift network provides a further inversion of the signal and provides positive feedback at its operating frequency.

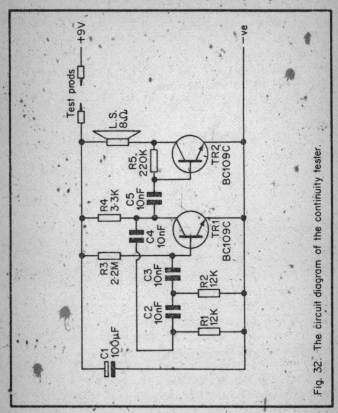

Fig. 32. The circuit diagram of the continuity tester.

The output from the oscillator is fed to a high gain common emitter stage via DC blocking capacitor C5. A loudspeaker forms the collector load for this stage, and biasing is provided by R5. C1 provides supply decoupling.

The test prods are connected in the positive supply lead, and so the circuit is only supplied with power when there is electrical continuity between the two test prods. The current consumption of the circuit is quite high at about 25mA., and the unit has been purposely designed this way. Units such as this should obviously only produce an audio tone if there is a very low impedance across the test prods, as otherwise misleading results could easily be obtained. As the circuit has a fairly high current consumption there will be quite a high voltage drop across any resistance between the two test prods. This voltage drop will prevent the circuit from producing the audio tone. On the prototype an audio tone would only be produced if the resistance across the test prods was less than about 50 ohms.

Despite the fairly high current consumption the unit is economical to run since current is only consumed when there is continuity between the test prods. For obvious reasons, no on/off switch is required.

Construction

This circuit can be built using any normal method of construction and the component layout is not at all critical. The components in the phase shift network do not need to have close tolerances.

Continuity Tester Components

Resistors. All miniature ¼ watt 5 or 10%
R1   12k.
R2   12k.
R3   2.2 Meg.
R4   3.3k.
R5   220k.

Capacitors.
C1   100mfd. 10v.w.
C2   10nf plastic foil.
C3   10nf plastic foil.
C4   10nf plastic foil.
C5   10nf plastic foil.

Semiconductors.
Tr1   BC109C.
Tr2   BC109C.

Miscellaneous.
8 ohm impedance loudspeaker.
Case, test leads and prods, 9 volt battery and connector, wire,
etc.

Power Supply Unit

When building and testing electronic equipment it is very useful to have a workshop power supply. Batteries can be used
when testing out modest equipment, but this can become
rather expensive in the long term. Larger items of equipment
are often unsuitable for battery operation, even just for testing
purposes, and a mains power supply of some sort is then
essential. The unit described here provides an output voltage
which is adjustable over a range of a little more than 5 to 30
volts. The maximum output current can be either 500mA. or
1 Amp. depending upon the mains transformer used. Output
current limiting is incorporated in the design which is therefore capable of withstanding output short circuits without
sustaining any damage. With maximum output voltage there
is a drop in the output potential of only about 600mV. When
the output current is taken from zero to full load. This is not
as good as the most sophisticated of laboratory power supplies,
but is much more than adequate for normal amateur
requirements.

Apart from use as a workshop power supply, the unit can also
be used as the power source for the 10 Watt power amplifier
which was described in Chapter 2 (either the mono or the
stereo version). The circuit diagram of the unit is provided in
Fig. 33.

The output from T1 is full wave push-pull rectified by D1
and D2, and then well smoothed by C1. If R1, R2, and Tr1
are ignored for the time being, the output from C1 is used to

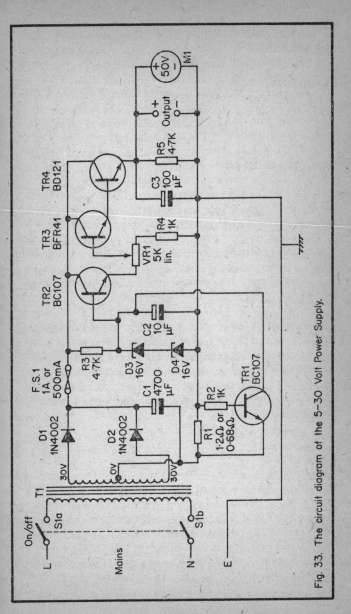

Fig. 33. The circuit diagram of the 5–30 Volt Power Supply.

125

feed a simple Zener stabiliser circuit which utilizes R3, D3, and D4. A Zener voltage of 32 volts is required here, and this has to be made by connecting two 16 volt Zeners in series as 32 volt components are not available. C2 smoothes any noise spikes which are produced across the Zener diodes.

The output from the Zener stabiliser is fed to a potential divider comprising VR1 and R4 via an emitter follower buffer stage (Tr2). A voltage range of approximately 6 to 31 volts is available at the slider of VR1, but this is at a high impedance. Tr3 and Tr4 are used as a Darlington Pair emitter follower buffer stage which is interposed between VR1 slider and the output of the power supply. This buffer stage provides a low impedance output which is easily capable of providing the required high output currents with little voltage drop. There is, however, a voltage drop of about 1 volt or so across the base — emitter junctions of Tr3 and Tr4 even with zero output, and so the output voltage range of the unit is from about 5 to 30 volts.

R5 forms a load resistor for Tr3 and Tr4, and this is necessary as the output stage will not operate properly with very low output currents. R5 ensures that there is always an adequate current flowing through the output stage when the supply is in use. C3 provides final smoothing of the output. M1 is a standard moving coil panel voltmeter which is used to monitor the output potential.

Current Limit

There is quite a high risk of output short circuits occuring with a general purpose workshop power supply such as this, and so it is virtually essential to incorporate some form of electronic output overload protection circuit. Ordinary fuses are not really suitable as they would probably not act fast enough to protect the output transistor, and it would be costly and time consuming to keep replacing them anyway.

In this circuit the type of overload protection that is employed is output current limiting. This is where the output current is limited to a value which is approximately equal to the designed maximum output current of the supply, even if a short circuit is applied to the output. The supply is unaffected by the current limit circuit until the limit current is reached.

R1, R2, and Tr1 provide the current limiting. Normally Tr1 is cut off, but it will be switched on if the voltage across R1 reaches about 0.66 volts. The value of R1 is chosen so that such a voltage is produced when the designed maximum output current is reached. Thus Tr1 is normally cut off and has no effect on the circuit, but when the output is overloaded it is turned on and shunts the Zener diode. This reduces the output voltage to a level which prevents any significant increase in the output current.

For a maximum output current of 500mA. R1 should be given a value of 1.2 ohms and T1 should be rated at 500mA. For a maximum output current of 1 Amp. R1 should have a value of 0.68 ohms and T1 should have a current rating of 1 Amp. R1 should be rated at ½ watt or more for the 500mA. version of the supply, and 1 watt or more for the 1 Amp. version. If difficulty in obtaining a 0.68 ohm resistor is experienced, then two 1.2 ohm components wired in parallel can be used here. T1 should be a good quality type as these are usually conservatively rated and will provide good and reliable results. Some inexpensive types are rather optimistically rated, and could give mediocre results and comparatively poor reliability.

R2 may seem to play no useful part in the circuit, but it is needed in order to protect the base emitter junction of Tr1. Without this resistor it is possible that the voltage across R1 could reach about a volt or so before the current limit circuit became effective, with Tr1 being destroyed in consequence. R2 provides current limiting and so prevents Tr1 being destroyed in the event of an excessive voltage across R1.

Construction

One advantage of this simple type of regulator over most of the more sophisticated configurations is that it cannot become unstable, and that the component layout is not critical. However, remember that fairly heavy current can flow in certain parts of the circuit, and so circuit boards and connecting wires must be adequate to handle these currents. If the unit is housed in a metal case this must be connected to the mains earth. In fact any exposed metal parts must be properly earthed.

Tr4 requires a substantial amount of heatsinking, and if the unit has a large metal case or chassis this can be used as the heatsink, provided it is possible to mount Tr1 in good thermal contact with the case or chassis (i.e. do not mount Tr1 on a painted or plastic covered surface). Alternatively a large size commercially produced heatsink can be used. In either case it will probably be necessary to insulate Tr1 from the heatsink using the usual mica washer and insulating bushes. Make quite sure that this insulation is effective as if it should happen to be faulty a short circuit will be placed on the unregulated output from D1 and D2, and the current limit circuitry would not be effective against such a short circuit. This is why fuse FS1 has been included in the unit.

If the unit is to be used as the power supply for the 10 Watt power amplifier described in Chapter 2 it is not necessary to include M1 in the circuit. A multimeter can then be used to monitor the output voltage while VR1 is adjusted for the correct output potential (30 volts). VR1 can be replaced by a preset type, of course. The 500mA. version of the supply is suitable for powering a mono amplifier, while the 1 Amp. version will be required to properly supply a stereo amplifier.

Power Supply Unit Components

Resistors.
R1   1.2 ohms 1 watt or more or 0.68 ohms ½ watt or more
      (see text).
R2   1k ¼ watt 5 or 10%.
R3   4.7k ¼ watt 5 or 10%.
R4   1k ¼ watt 5%.
R5   4.7k ¼ watt 5 or 10%
VR1 5k lin. carbon.

Capacitors.
C1   4,700mfd. 50v.w.
C2   10mfd. 40v.w.
C3   100mfd. 40v.w.

Semiconductors.
Tr1   BC107.
Tr2   BC107.
Tr3   BFR41.
Tr4   BD121.
D1   1N4002.
D2   1N4002.
D3   BZY88C 16V.
D4   BZY88C 16V.

Transformer.
Standard mains primary, 30V – OV – 30V secondary rated
at 500mA, or 1 Amp (see text).

Switch
S1   DPST toggle type.

Meter.
M1   Panel type moving coil voltmeter, 50 volts FSD.

Miscellaneous.
1 Amp fuse and holder, case, heatsink for Tr4 (if necessary),
output sockets, control knob, connecting wire, etc.

AF Signal Generator

This is probably the most popular item of test equipment, which is not surprising as it is needed when testing most parameters of audio equipment (frequency response, voltage gain, harmonic distortion, etc.), and it can also be very useful when fault finding on audio equipment and other gear. The circuit of Fig. 34 is for a simple sinewave generator which covers a frequency range of 30Hz to 30kHz, and has a low distortion content on the output (less than 0.1% at 1kHz on the prototype). It is therefore suitable for most audio testing.

The circuit is a conventional Wien Bridge oscillator type, and an IC operational amplifier forms the basis of the unit. It is used in the non-inverting mode, and it is powered from dual balanced 9 volt supplies. Positive feedback is provided by the Wien Bridge network which consists of VR1a, VR1b, R1, R3, and whichever two capacitors are switched into circuit by S1a and S1b.

VR1 is the fine frequency control, and this enables the output frequency to be tuned over each range. S1 is the course frequency control, and this provides three ranges by allowing one of three sets of capacitors to be switched into the Wien network. The ranges covered are as follows:— Range 1, 30Hz to 300Hz: Range 2, 300Hz to 3kHz: Range 3, 3kHz to 30kHz.

In order to obtain a good output waveform having high purity it is necessary for the gain of the circuit to be accurately maintained at a level which is only just sufficient to produce oscillation. If the gain is slightly too low the circuit will fail to oscillate, and if it is too high the output will clip and be considerably distorted. The required voltage gain is approximately three times, but the exact figure varies slightly with various settings of VR1. The gain cannot be preset therefore, and some form of automatic gain control (AGC) is required.

The closed loop voltage gain of the circuit is determined by the values of the two resistors in the negative feedback loop

130

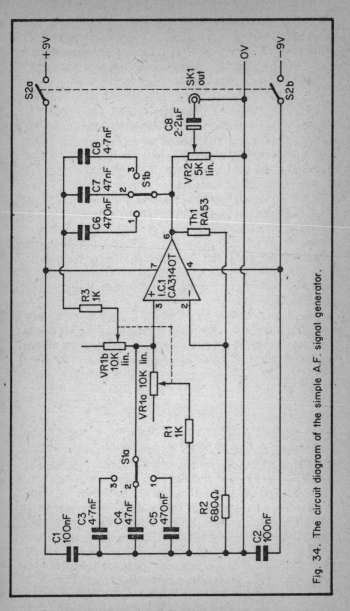

Fig. 34. The circuit diagram of the simple A.F. signal generator.

131

(Th1 and R2), and is equal to Th1 + R2 divided by R2. Th1 is an ordinary negative temperature coefficient thermistor, but it is not a component of the type which is designed to respond to changes in the ambient temperature. It is a self heating type of high sensitivity which is used to sense the current in the feedback circuit. If a high current flows, such as when the amplitude of the output signal is high, the temperature of the thermistor is increased, with a consequent fall in its resistance. This reduces the gain of the circuit, and thus also reduces the amplitude of the output, and prevents clipping of the waveform. If the amplitude of the output signal should fall for some reason, or even cease completely, the current flow through the thermistor will fall or cease altogether, which in turn causes its resistance to rise. This increases the gain of the circuit and so produces an output of the correct level. In this way the thermistor maintains the gain of the circuit at just the right level. It also stabilises the output level so that once a certain output level has been set, it will remain constant at this level regardless of the setting of VR1 or S1.

The actual output amplitude of the oscillator is a little over 1 volt rms, but this can be attenuated by adjusting VR2 if necessary. C9 provides DC blocking at the output. C1 and C2 are supply decoupling capacitors and S2 is the on/off switch.

Construction

Electrically the construction of this project is not at all critical, and should be quite straightforward. From the mechanical point of view it is advisable to use a case having a fairly large front panel so that a large calibrated dial can be marked around the control knob of VR1. Calibrating the unit accuratel might prove to be rather difficult if limited test gear is available It will of course be quite easy if access can be gained to a suitable frequency meter. If a suitable oscilloscope and an accurately calibrated AF generator are available, the unit can be calibrated using the Lissajous figure method.

If only an accurately calibrated signal generator is available, an aural method can be used. To do this it is necessary to connect each generator to a crystal earpiece, amplifier and speaker combination, or something of this nature so that the output signals can be heard. If, for example, the point on the dial which corresponds to 100Hz is to be located, the ready calibrated generator is adjusted to a frequency of 100Hz and then the other generator is adjusted to produce a note of the same frequency. The dial can then be marked appropriately at the position indicated by the pointer. Of course, any calibration points within the audio frequency spectrum can be located using the same method.

In the event that a suitably calibrated signal generator is not available an alternative is a musical instrument of some kind which can be used in conjunction with the table below to provide notes of known frequency.

Note	Frequency
c (Middle)	262Hz.
d	294Hz.
e	330Hz.
f	349Hz.
g	392Hz.
a	440Hz.
b	494Hz.

Successive octaves above this double in frequency, and octaves below this halve in frequency.

Note that the scale on the generator will be logarithmic and not linear. One scale can be used for all three ranges provided close tolerance capacitors are used in the Wien network, as specified.

A.F. Signal Generator

Resistors.
R1   1k ¼ watt 5%.
R2   680 ohms ¼ watt 5 or 10%.
R3   1k ¼ watt 5%.
VR1 10k plus 10k lin. carbon dual gang.
VR2 5k lin. carbon.

Capacitors.
C1   100nf plastic foil.
C2   100nf plastic foil.
C3   4.7nf plastic foil 2% or better.
C4   47nf plastic foil 2% or better.
C5   470nf plastic foil 2% or better.
C6   470nf plastic foil 2% or better.
C7   47nf plastic foil 2% or better.
C8   4.7nf plastic foil 2% or better.
C9   2.2mfd. plastic foil.

Semiconductors.
IC1 CA314OT.

Thermistor
Th1 RA53.

Switch.
S1   3 way 4 pole-rotary type (only two poles used).
S2   DPST toggle type.

Miscellaneous.
Two 9 volt batteries and connectors to suit.
Case, control knobs, component panel, output socket,
connecting wire, etc.

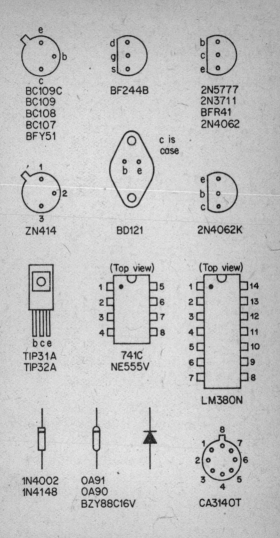

Fig. 35. Transistor base diagrams, I.C. pin out diagrams,
and diode leadout diagrams.

135

Notes

Notes

Notes

OTHER BOOKS OF INTEREST

222: SOLID STATE SHORT WAVE RECEIVERS FOR BEGINNERS
AUTHOR: R.A. PENFOLD

PRICE: 95p

ISBN: 0 900162 62 7

96 Pages

Approx. Size: 180 x 105 mm

There is a strange fascination in listening to a broadcast which has been transmitted from a station that may be many thousands of miles away across the other side of the world. This has helped to make short wave listening one of the most popular and interesting branches of electronics and for this reason, is an excellent way of capturing the interest of a beginner. In fact, very many enthusiasts and "Hams" have been introduced to the hobby in this way.

In this book, Mr R.A. Penfold, who is a very experienced author and has regularly written for many of the popular electronic monthly magazines, has designed and developed several modern solid state short wave receiver circuits that will give a fairly high level of performance, despite the fact that they use only relatively few and inexpensive components.

223: 50 PROJECTS USING IC CA3130
AUTHOR: R.A. PENFOLD

PRICE: 95p

ISBN: 0 900162 65 1

112 Pages

Approx. Size: 180 x 105 mm

The CA3130 is currently one of the more advanced operational amplifiers that is available to the home constructor. This means that it is often capable of a higher level of performance than many other devices and that it often needs fewer ancillary components.

In this book, the author has designed and developed a number of interesting and useful projects which are divided into five general categories:

I   — Audio Projects
II   — R.F. Projects
III   — Test Equipment
IV   — Household Projects
V   — Miscellaneous Projects

An ideal book for both the beginner and more advance enthusiast alike.

224: 50 CMOS IC PROJECTS
AUTHOR: R.A. PENFOLD

PRICE: 95p

ISBN: 0 900162 64 3

112 Pages

Approx. Size: 180 x 105 mm

CMOS IC's are probably the most versatile range of digital devices for use by the amateur enthusiast. They are suitable for an extraordinary wide range of applications and are now also some of the most inexpensive and easily available types of IC.

Mr R.A. Penfold has designed and developed a number of interesting and useful projects which are divided into four general categories:

I   – Multivibrators
II   – Amplifiers and Oscillators
III   – Trigger Devices
IV   – Special Devices

A must for any electronic enthusiast's library.

226: HOW TO BUILD ADVANCED SHORT WAVE RECEIVERS

AUTHOR: R.A. PENFOLD   PRICE: £1.20
ISBN: 0 900162 67 8   128 Pages
Approx. Size: 180 x 105 mm

Although many short wave listeners and radio amateurs use commercial equipment these days, greater satisfaction and enjoyment can be gained from the hobby by using home constructed equipment. Using ready made S.W. gear does not give any insight into the way the apparatus functions and by building one's own equipment, it is virtually inevitable that a reasonable understanding of the techniques involved will be grasped. Obviously, such an understanding is very helpful when it comes to actually using a finished receiver, and it should enable the operator to obtain optimum results from the set. In this book, Mr R.A. Penfold gives full practical constructional details of a number of receivers which should have levels of performance at least equal to that of commercially built sets of similar complexity. Furthermore, the home constructed receiver is likely to cost very much less than it's ready made equivalent.

Also included are a number of add-on circuits, such as Q-Multiplier, S-Meter, Noise Limiter, etc., which can be used to aid and improve reception when using the receivers.

227: BEGINNERS GUIDE TO BUILDING ELECTRONIC PROJECTS

AUTHOR: R.A. PENFOLD   PRICE: £1.25
ISBN: 0 900162 68 6   112 Pages
Approx. Size: 180 x 105 mm

The purpose of this book is to enable the complete beginner to tackle the practical side of electronics, so that he or she can confidently build the electronic projects that are regularly featured in the popular magazines and books.

Subjects such as component identification, tools, soldering, various constructional methods (Matrixboard, Veroboard, P.C.B.) cases, legends etc. are covered in details and practical examples in the form of simple projects are given.

Written by Mr R.A. Penfold who is a very experienced author of many books and who also writes regularly for the popular electronics magazines.

An absolutely invaluable book for all beginners in electronics.

BP45:   PROJECTS IN OPTO-ELECTRONICS
AUTHOR: R.A. PENFOLD

PRICE: £1.25
ISBN: 0 85934 049 X
112 Pages
Approx. Size: 180 × 105 mm

Any electronic or electrical device that responds to light may be considered to come under the heading of Opto-Electronic devices.

Although many people tend to take Opto-Electronic devices and circuits for granted, it is hoped that this book will show even the most experienced reader that they can be used in a surprisingly wide range of applications.

The purpose of this book is to describe a number of projects which may be of interest to all electronics enthusiasts. Included are simple circuits using ordinary light emitting diodes (L.E.D.s) as well as more sophisticated designs such as Infra Red Transmitters and Detectors, Modulated Light Transmission and also Photographic projects etc.

Please note overleaf is a list of other titles that are available in our range of Radio and Electronics Books.

These should be available from all good Booksellers, Radio Component Dealers and Mail Order Companies.

However, should you experience difficulty in obtaining any title in your area, then please write directly to the publisher enclosing payment to cover the cost of the book plus adequate postage.

If you would like a Catalogue of our complete range of Radio and Electronics Books, please send a Stamped Addressed Envelope.

BERNARD BABANI (publishing) LTD
THE GRAMPIANS
SHEPHERDS BUSH ROAD
LONDON W6 7NF
ENGLAND

BERNARD BABANI (Publishing) LTD

The Grampians, Shepherd's Bush Road, London W6 7NF, England
Telephone: 01–603 2581/7296